CHEMICALS IN WESTERN EUROPE:
1850–1914

CHEMICALS IN WESTERN EUROPE:
1850–1914

An economic study of technical change

PAUL M. HOHENBERG

Stanford University, Stanford, Calif.

RAND McNALLY & COMPANY – CHICAGO

RAND McNALLY & COMPANY – CHICAGO – 1967

Library of Congress Catalog Card Number: 67-21969

PUBLISHERS:
RAND McNALLY & COMPANY – CHICAGO

SOLE DISTRIBUTORS FOR THE EASTERN HEMISPHERE:
NORTH-HOLLAND PUBLISHING COMPANY–AMSTERDAM

PRINTED IN THE NETHERLANDS

For my Mother and to the
Memory of my Father

Preface

My interest in the growth of chemical production in Europe dates back to a seminar at the Fletcher School, Tufts University. It grew, there and at the Massachusetts Institute of Technology, under the guidance and encouragement of Charles P. Kindleberger.

Many others, on both sides of the ocean and on both coasts of the American continent, have also given of their help and encouragement and, not least, of their critical thought. A very partial list of those who helped me gather information in Europe includes Messrs. C. Morazé, R. Robin, J. Bouvier, M. Lagache, T. Markovitch, E. Sohmen, C. Menzi, and A. Bürgin. I am also indebted to the management of the following companies for access to material in their possession: Geigy, Sandoz, Höchst, the BASF, St. Gobain, and the Union des Industries Chimiques in Paris.

It is impossible to mention all the teachers and colleagues, at MIT and Stanford, whose patient but critical questions forced me to think the argument through a number of times. I think particularly of David Landes, Moses Abramovitz, and the other members of the Berkeley–Stanford colloquium in economic history. I hasten to add that the people and institutions mentioned here bear no responsibility for errors, either of omission or commission.

I am happy to acknowledge the help of several institutional sponsors, who turn out on inspection to have a common origin in support provided by the Ford Foundation. My research was helped by a grant from MIT's Department of Economics, and I wrote the study while the holder of a Ford Dissertation Fellowship. Finally, I thank the Research Center in Economic Growth at Stanford for providing the financial help and institutional support which enabled me to revise the manuscript.

I am indebted to Mrs. Mary Johnson for her efficiency and care in typing the manuscript, and to Mrs. Linda Brownrigg for editorial assistance.

Palo Alto, September 1966   Paul M. Hohenberg

Contents

Introduction

The Great War of 1914–1918 showed the world that a new generation of industries had come of age, supplementing older established sectors they were soon in part to displace. To be sure, textiles, coal mining, iron and steel manufacture and transformation, and food processing still occupied most of the labor force in large-scale industry. However, many of the bottlenecks of wartime production involved light metals and alloys, new types of vehicles, equipment and instruments, and a wide variety of chemically processed materials such as liquid fuels, explosives, drugs, and synthetic materials. Of the industries pushed into the foreground of attention, none had more numerous and varied connections with the productive process than the manufacture of industrial chemicals. The chemical industry was not new in western Europe, but it took the war to bring out that here were more than a few ill-smelling factories producing mysterious and noxious witches' brews. Not only were the industry's products greatly needed, but it seemed to have a remarkable capacity to expand its range of activity to meet new needs and shortages.

This book is an economic study of the European chemical industry from about 1850 to the outbreak of World War I. It focuses on France, Germany, and Switzerland, casting only sidelong glances at Great Britain and Belgium, the other countries in which the industry enjoyed any considerable development. For the purposes of this study, the chemical industry is defined rather narrowly; I am excluding, for example, the production of rubber, petroleum products, soap, and explosives. Definitional problems of this type should prove minor in relation to the central concern of the book, which is to characterize and explain economic performance rather than to measure it. They do, however, make it difficult to use such limited quantitative data as are available regarding the size and rate of growth of the industry.

Anyone familiar with the literature of industrial history will no doubt grant the need for making what should be an obvious point: economic studies of an industry gain from being cast in the form of answers to one or more questions, preferably specific and explicit ones. As the book will show, even this necessary step does not ensure full and definite answers, but it brings out, at least, the degree of success achieved in coming to grips with the problem posed. There is, to be sure, room for answering the open-ended question 'what happened?', especially when new or unfamiliar material is presented, and it is hoped that the book makes some modest contributions in this direction. The main emphasis, however, will be on two questions:

1. What factors account for the relative performance of the industry in the three countries?

2. What impact did the industry have on the process of economic growth in the three countries?

These are rather straightforward questions. They may be rephrased even more simply, perhaps, to read:

1. Why did the industry grow more rapidly here than there?

2. What difference did it make to the economies?

Putting the questions in this form may give a clue to the fact that the answers are likely to be less easy than the questions. Scientific method is justly wary of questions containing too much 'why?', although the social scientist, and the economic historian in particular, seeks explanations of what has happened to compensate for his inability to recreate phenomena in the laboratory or to accumulate truly comparable observations outside it.

Specifically, the questions imply a theory of the growth of firms and industries on the one hand, and on the other a theoretical model of the interaction between sectors of the economy in the process of economic growth. While there is no shortage of work on either score, contact with an actual historical situation has convinced me that it falls short of providing an operational framework. The study therefore incorporates attempts to add to the corpus of theoretical work some reflections on growth and on the process of technical change.

In addition to specifying the scope of the study, it may be well to set out certain general views about the process of growth that underlie what follows. The reader may find some of them obvious and others highly doubtful. They are not original and do not add up to anything like a consistent theory. But they are implicit throughout the book and hardly spelled out or argued again.

I believe that the process of economic growth is associated much more closely with more productive use of economic resources than with their accumulation. Thus, of the three ways in which growth may occur, one should stress reallocation of resources and improved productivity of given combinations of resources over increases in their amount. It should be noted that reallocation and changes in efficiency are not nearly so separable as production theory often suggests. Perhaps the sharp distinction between movements along a curve (here the isoquant) and shifts of the curve has been taken over too literally from the theory of demand. In both cases the distinction is valid only where information is full and free, but relaxing this assumption has more tangible implications in the case of production. The matter is taken up again in more detail in Chapter 3. For the present, it is enough to note that a growing economy is characterized by relatively frequent and sizeable change. At the microeconomic level, this suggests that an important condition for firms in such an economy is the ability to deal efficiently with change, and, if possible, to initiate it of themselves. Perhaps this type of dynamic efficiency is more important than minimization of costs under static technical and market conditions. At the aggregate level, growth depends on the elasticity with which resources can be reallocated between economic units and on the rate at which economically useful knowledge is produced and then effectively incorporated in the economic process.

Looking now at the process of economic growth over time, I think it is most fruitful to see the development of an economy as a cumulative but not irreversible process. Growth is indeed a powerful force promoting further growth, and it is useful to think of a progressive economy, i.e., one in which the process and expectation of growth are built into the behavior of economic units. But I reject the model of a one-time shift from stagnation to progressiveness implied by the notion of a take-off. Such a position is virtually inescapable for the student of France in the 19th century, since he is faced with a clearly intermediate case, one in which steady growth was combined with persistent resistance to rapid modernization. Furthermore, I am concerned with economies already engaged in the process of industrialization and with the role of a particular industry in accelerating or retarding it. For the problem to be non-trivial, I must assume that there are obstacles to growth, or at least postulate the need for continued autonomous stimuli to further progress. What I seek is not *the* key to growth, *the* sector or impulse necessary and sufficient for a progressive economy. The task is a more modest one. It is that of identifying, documenting, and evaluating mechanisms by which firms and industries grow, and by which they in turn provide a stimulus for further growth to other parts of the economy. In this connection, an industry may be called 'leading' if its own growth is *relatively* autonomous, i.e., independent of particularly favorable environmental conditions, and if, in addition, it provides *relatively* strong stimuli to the rest of the economy.

The major theoretical hypothesis on which the book is based should be stated at the outset, with the hope that the reader will reserve judgment and let the study argue for the author that the following propositions are neither wrong nor trivial.

> Technical progress is in substantial part the fruit of resources devoted to the production of knowledge. The extent of such *technical effort* (as this activity is called hereafter) varies widely among firms and industries. Relatively great technical effort is conducive to rapid growth for the firm or industry in which the activity takes place. It also gives rise to technical progress which is implemented elsewhere in the economy. In this way even a small sector may have substantial growth-promoting effects.

Since the above hypothesis grew out of studying the chemical industry in 19th-century western Europe, it is not surprising that the evidence appears to fit it rather well. The purpose of the book is, however, to break out of the closed loop formed by one case and one hypothesis, and to argue for the need to treat technical change as endogenous, given its central role in the process of economic growth.

I have tried to make this an exercise in interpretive economic history as well as a case study for certain observations about growth in industrializing countries. As economic history it may seem insufficiently quantitative to many readers. The reason is not that I eschew the use of numerical data, but that I have wanted to go further than the sparse and often inappropriate quantitative record would permit. In the last analysis, the extent to which one uses data which are available as proxies for variables one cannot measure must remain partly a matter of taste. I can only say that increased familiarity with the historical record has not diminished my natural reluctance to make numbers do for one another. On the other hand, the monograph is not intended as a descriptive study of the industry. Historical material is presented chiefly as it pertains to the hypotheses being investigated, the exception being summary accounts of technical and economic developments in the first part of the book. The interested reader is referred to the sources discussed in the text for fuller descriptions and other analytical approaches.

Following the discussion of sources and a sketch of technical developments, the book turns to the three country cases, and attempts to explain differences in performance by the market environment facing the industry in each one. The failure of this attempt leads to the development of 'technical effort' and the 'knowledge-centered firm' as explanatory concepts, and to further analysis of the chemical industry. Then, the role of the industry in the growth process is taken up. Again, the concept of technical effort is found helpful in providing a meaningful approach. The broader implications of the central hypothesis are examined in the concluding chapter.

PART I

Growth and technical progress in the chemical industry

Sources of information
and a survey of technical developments to 1914

Proceeding from the general to the particular, the kinds of sources on which this study draws include literature on European industrialization and on the different countries, studies of the industry and its technology and of related sectors, histories of individual firms, and biographies of entrepreneurs and technical men. I have drawn on three comprehensive and basic books that also summarize much of the literature: the studies of L. F. Haber and J. J. Beer, and the remarkable essay by David Landes.[*,1])

With respect to the industrialization of western Europe in the later 19th century, there is no need to recall here the standard sources. The essay by Landes referred to above is particularly valuable, in view of the technical emphasis of the present study. Recent works stressing the quantitative evidence of industrial growth in France and Germany are those of Markovitch and Hoffmann[2]). Two sources of information which deserve brief mention are the Universal Expositions and Parliamentary inquiries. The former, which were of great importance in the life of the 19th century, gave rise to monographs on the state of industry in general, and of its various branches in the countries of Europe and in the United States. These reports reviewed recent technical developments, gave spotty data on the quantitative progress of the industry, and discussed its prospects and problems. The Parliamentary inquiries, though not so useful for France as for Great Britain, give insight into such questions as agricultural fertilizers and commercial policy.

Historical studies of the chemical industry tend to be descriptive[3]). Few, if any, repose on primary sources, so that all rely on the scarce and inadequate data available from official sources. This is especially true of

---

* Numbered footnotes appear at the back of each chapter; a short form is used and the reader is referred to the bibliography for publication details.

quantitative evidence such as production figures which cover only a few products. Official data refer mainly to foreign trade, occasionally to consumption of basic raw materials and energy or to numbers and size (persons employed) of establishments. However, many chemical products were not traded much across national borders, and the census data suffer from problems of definition of the industry. Costs have been studied in only a few cases, such as the two competing soda processes and the manufacture of sulfuric acid. A number of 'economic' studies have been made, some of which purported to approach the subject as this study does, i.e., to examine the effect of the chemical industry on the economy. In fact, such studies usually summarize the available statistical data and discuss the factors responsible for the growth or lack of it of the industry itself. There are also many popular accounts of the importance of chemicals and chemical science to industry and everyday life. For France, the most careful studies of the industry have been made by geographers, although these, too, remain largely descriptive. Histories of technology tend to stress invention over diffusion of techniques and economic factors, while technical reference works are vague or unreliable regarding the historical development of a process or product. Nevertheless, both are useful.

As for sectors presumably influenced by the chemical industry, it has not been possible to survey the literature as systematically as in the chemical sector itself, especially not the technical literature. But little work seems as yet to have been done on the linkages between industries, especially of the growth-inducing or innovation-spreading type with which we are concerned.

My attempts to obtain information on the pre-World War I period from important firms in the three countries met with only partial success. In no case was it possible to gain access to firm archives. Some early annual reports were available, but these furnished little information, as it was not then the practice in Europe to divulge much to stockholders. Company histories are commonly available and vary widely both in quality and in scope. Though they provide valuable information, they are biased for at least two reasons. First, they are written by the company or at its invitation, and are not critical in the academic sense. But in addition, they are available only for successful companies, and fail to illuminate the often more interesting failures. Considerable biographical information is available, some of it uncritical, for leading entrepreneurial and scientific figures in Germany and Switzerland, but little for France.

1. Summary of the technical history

This survey will give only the broad lines of changing chemical technology in the period from 1850 to 1914, chiefly as an aid to the subsequent economic discussion. The subjects covered are soda and the heavy chemicals sector, the development of synthetic organic chemicals and the coal-tar industry, chemical fertilizers, and the early uses of electricity for chemical processes. The discussion will cut across country lines and include British and Belgian developments where appropriate[4]).

1.1. Soda and related heavy chemicals

In 1850 the Leblanc process for sodium carbonate (soda ash) was at the center of the chemical industry. It was coupled with the production of sulfuric acid and used much of the output of this second important industrial chemical. Soda ash, or soda, found a wide variety of uses in and out of the chemical industry. The economics of the Leblanc process and its by-products are summarized in Fig. 1. The processes for sulfuric acid and

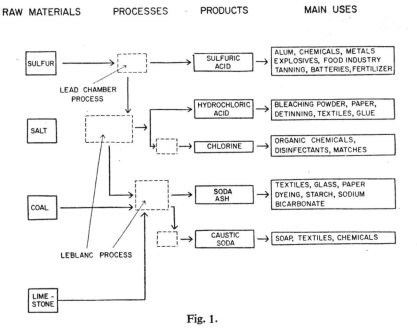

Fig. 1.

Table 1.   Improvements in sulfuric acid and Leblanc soda manufacture, 1830–1887.

Product	Year	Process change	Significance	Country
Sulfuric Acid	1833	Perret use of pyrites	Frees industry from reliance on sulfur	F
	1842	Gay–Lussac Tower	Improve acid process	F
	1861	Glover Tower		GB
Hydrochloric Acid	1863	Gossage Tower	Prevents pollution, recovers HCl	GB
Chlorine	1870	Weldon process	Bleaching powder	GB
	1883	Deacon process	Bleaching powder	GB
	1887	Weldon–Péchiney process	Bleaching powder	F
Sulfur	1885	Chance process	Recovers sulfur lost from Leblanc process	GB

soda were known before 1800, but significant improvements continued to be made throughout the century, chiefly in England but in France as well. The most important of these are summarized in Table 1.

In 1863 Ernest Solvay, a Belgian, developed the ammonia–soda process for which many people had been searching, some with partial success. His first plants were installed in 1873. This process triggered a series of developments that culminated in the disappearance of the Leblanc process after 1900. The battle was hard fought, and Leblanc producers showed considerable ingenuity in lowering costs, chiefly by perfecting the recovery of by-products, as shown in Table 1. But even the increased demand for chlorine, which is not produced by the Solvay process, could not save the old method once electrolytic chlorine became available. The heavy chemicals industry of 1914 can be summarized by Fig. 2.

Two aspects of Fig. 2 are of interest. The first is that by 1913 the basic processes used were the same as they are today, although many improvements have been made. The second is the lessened interdependence of processes on each other as compared to the earlier period shown in Fig. 1. This tendency has become stronger in the chemical industry in more recent times. Technical progress is aimed at increasing flexibility and control over output by developing a specific process for a product. Joint products and by-products still exist, and the use of chemicals to make other chemicals creates further economic ties, but this is less im-

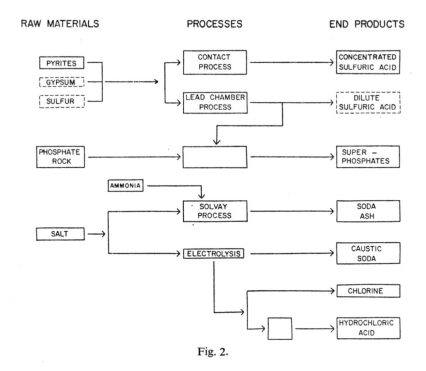

Fig. 2.

portant today than it was in the 19th century. In the earlier time, technical effort was directed at perfecting by-product recovery as a way to increase the efficiency of an existing process. Though this involved scientific research, it was really a pre-scientific approach. Decisive progress often proved to be the result not of continued pressure at the margin of the existing technology, but of an entirely new departure requiring substantial basic and applied research.

The production of superphosphates from phosphate rock, though not part of this group, has been included in Fig. 2 because this replaced the Leblanc process as the main outlet for sulfuric acid from the chamber process. Here, too, the development of a new process for acid spurred technical change, but the result was coexistence based on specialization, and not the disappearance of the old method as had happened in the case of soda. Chamber acid continued to be produced, largely for superphosphate use, while the contact process furnished concentrated acid for the production of organic chemicals and other uses.

1.2. Coal-tar and organic chemicals

In 1850 coal-tar was available in considerable quantities as a by-product of the destructive distillation of coal to produce gas for urban lighting. It was considered largely a nuisance, despite limited applications for certain constituents. Thus naphtha was used as the original solvent for rubber by MacIntosh for waterproofing cloth, and wood was impregnated with creosote as early as 1838. Within three decades coal-tar had become a valuable raw material, entering international trade in large amounts and subject to strong price fluctuations and crises of the sort familiar in markets for basic commodities. The chief development initiating this rise was the process for fractional distillation of coal-tar, developed in 1848. Fig. 3 gives a schematic picture of the constituents of coal-tar and some of their uses. The dates are bench-marks for applications before 1914 and are often not precise, as must needs be the case in discussions of technological history.

The gas industry, and with it the production of coal-tar, was most highly developed in England, which exported tar and the products of its distillation. The production of metallurgical coke also involved coal dis-

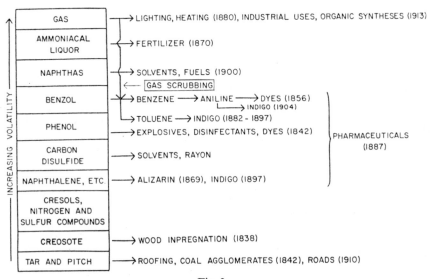

Fig. 3.

tillation, but until the 1880's the by-products were not recovered. By-product recovery ovens were invented in France and England in 1866, but perfected in Germany, for reasons that are not entirely clear but will be discussed later (see pp. 112 and 126).

As in the history of heavy chemicals, there are two distinct periods separated by a period of struggle and change. From 1860 to 1880 coal-tar was produced in gas works, chiefly in England, and the tar or the products of fractionation were used in chemical production, largely in Germany. After 1900, Germany produced tar and intermediates from coke ovens, obtaining additional benzol from the scrubbing of coke-oven gas after 1890. Gas works still produced some tar, but the English distilleries operated in part with imported tar. This complication was due to the use-centered location of coking plants, coupled with economies of scale in distillation. Great Britain exported coal and imported the crude tar, re-exporting distilled intermediate products.

In the eighties came changes in the gas industry, initiated by competition from electricity and the development of the gas mantle, with a resulting drop in the yield of tar due to higher carbonisation temperatures. This drop in the supply of coal-tar, coupled with greater demands from the chemical industry, hastened the adoption of by-product coke ovens in Germany. Later, the gas from coking was also recovered and used in blast furnaces and eventually for other purposes, including important chemical processes[5]).

The story of coal-tar derivatives is a complex one, since coal-tar was the chief source of raw materials for organic chemicals up to World War II. Before 1914 the main endproducts were dyestuffs, pharmaceuticals, and explosives. In this period, before the advent of catalytic syntheses, it was necessary to begin with the proper coal-tar fraction, of which some were available only in small amounts. Later it became possible to synthesize almost any organic intermediate from the most plentiful components, and gas and petroleum became important raw materials along with coal. But this period was only beginning at the outbreak of World War I.

The development of synthetic dyes, beginning in 1856 with the Englishman Perkin's discovery of mauveine, may be divided into three overlapping periods[6]).

The aniline dyes, of which mauveine was the first, held the field from 1856 to 1869 and continued to be produced later. They were not comparable to the best natural dyes in fastness, but gave many new and bright shades, and soon became cheaper than the natural products. After 1869, with the introduction of synthetic alizarin, a series of dyes was developed that replaced some natural dyes. This second phase was made possible, to a large extent, by Kekule's discovery of the structure of benzene, which opened the way for the use of structural formulas in organic chemistry and made systematic organic syntheses possible. The main holdout was indigo, and the third period saw the synthesis of this dye. It was first carried out by A. Baeyer in the laboratory in 1880, but did not become commercially feasible until 1897, after long and costly research in and out of industry.

This brief summary does not even begin to cover the many classes of dyes developed during this period. It should be mentioned here that early work on dyes was done chiefly in England and France[7]), whereas after 1865 the focus shifted to Germany and Switzerland, though the scientific effort was not so concentrated in these countries as was industrial development in this field. Production of dyes was also somewhat distributed, but was usually controlled, in France, England and other countries, by German or Swiss firms.

The production of synthetic pharmaceuticals was often closely related to work on dyestuffs. In fact, Perkin was attempting to synthesize quinine when he discovered mauveine. The first pharmaceuticals were sold by chemical companies in 1887. During this time the drug manufacturers used chemical technology to an increasing extent. Finally, after 1892 chemical companies began to manufacture serums and other products of a biochemical nature.

The industry that manufactured explosives lies outside the scope of this study, but its reliance on the chemical industry for raw materials became evident in a dramatic way during World War I.

1.3. Chemical fertilizers

In 1850 the use of chemical fertilizers was not widespread, although lively discussion and some experimentation on the problem of restoring nutrients to agricultural soil went on throughout Europe. Agricultural chemistry and the use of fertilizers are often associated with the name of Liebig, but at midcentury the British had progressed farther and had more accurate knowledge in this field than did the Germans. Some of Liebig's ideas on plant nutrition were wrong, though he was an important teacher of chemistry, organizer of research, and publicist, as well as a scientist.

Phosphates were beginning to be used, and in Britain Lawes began to market superphosphates (phosphate rock solubilized with sulfuric acid) in 1843. Sodium nitrate was imported in limited amounts. But the chief sources of plant nutrients from outside the agricultural sector consisted of bones, organic wastes, guano, and potash from plant ashes.

The use of phosphatic fertilizers increased rapidly in the countries of western Europe. At first soluble phosphates were ground and applied directly to the soil. Later, when these proved insufficient, rock phosphates were treated with acid. The discovery of large deposits of rock in North Africa led to a rapid expansion of the industry after 1890, especially in France, where production reached nearly 2 million tons per year in 1913. To this figure for French production must be added 735 000 tons of Thomas-meal, the phosphatic slag from the basic process for steel (Thomas–Gilchrist) of which 340 000 tons (net) were exported[8]).

The use of nitrogen fertilizers also grew steadily in this period, although less evenly between countries. Ammonium sulfate from coal-tar distillation and sodium nitrate from Chile were the important sources, replacing guano and organic wastes. Germany used over a million tons a year of these fertilizers in her agriculture in 1913; on the other hand, France consumed less than 400 000 tons. On an arable acreage basis the difference was almost tenfold[9]). A part of the French lag can be attributed to supply, particularly the failure to adopt by-product coking. But the major factor was low agricultural demand.

Around the turn of the century there was growing concern for the supply of nitrogen fertilizers in the long run, and intensified attempts to fix atmospheric nitrogen. Electrochemical methods were used first, the Birkeland–Eyde arc process in 1904 and the conversion of calcium carbide to calcium cyanamide around the same time. But these processes required very cheap electric power, and were scarcely competitive with natural sodium nitrate. A way had to be found to synthesize ammonia from nitrogen and hydrogen, available from air and/or coal gas.

The story of the ammonia synthesis is a dramatic one, and the first great triumph of the science of chemical engineering[10]). Before the process could be developed, a great deal of pure research had to be carried out on the long-known reaction, since it involved the use of catalysts, of extreme temperatures and pressures (for that time), and unfamiliar phys-icochemical principles. Le Chatelier, Nernst, and Haber were the im-portant workers. But it was the Badische Anilin- und Soda-Fabrik (BASF) and their chemist Carl Bosch who developed the process itself on an industrial scale[11]). In view of the technical problems involved, especially in the area of equipment, it is worth noting that the development from the first successful laboratory experiments to the first production on a com-mercial scale took only six years. The Oppau works were started in 1913. Though this has been challenged, it is fair to see this date, a year before the outbreak of the World War, as a great historic coincidence. It is alleged that the German military were unaware of the extent to which the supply of munitions depended on nitrates[12]). The BASF developed the process for oxidizing the Haber–Bosch ammonia to nitric acid only during 1914–15.

Potash, the third important fertilizer, became something of a German monopoly after 1870. The Stassfurt deposits furnished over 3 million tons annually by 1900, and even before then had totally replaced potash from wood ashes and seaweed[13]).

1.4. Electricity and chemical processes

It had long been known that chemical reactions could be carried out by means of electric currents, and that this was also a possible source of the concentrated energy required to achieve ultrahigh temperatures. But industrial applications of electricity became possible only after 1880, when efficient generators became available[14]). In the early days of the electrical industry, chemical uses were of great importance because transportation of current was not developed so rapidly as generation. Chemical processes were worked near sources of cheap hydroelectricity or, as in Germany, near brown coal which could be converted to electricity and thus used *in situ*. Three types of processes became important: electrolysis, electro-metallurgy, and electrothermal processing[15]).

The electrolysis of salt was the first process to become significant. It was developed around 1890 by Castner in England and by the Griesheim Company in Germany. The former was interested in metallic sodium used in making cyanides for processing gold ores. Griesheim, on the other hand, first electrolysed potassium chloride, in order to get potash, which could not be made by the Solvay process. The extension to electrolysis of salt (sodium chloride) came as a result of the demand for chlorine, not supplied by the ammonia–soda process. It is worth noting the important part played by the Solvay Company in the new process which was in part competitive with theirs. Chlorates were also made at this time by electrolysis.

Castner's attempts to make sodium metal, which led him to investigate electrolysis, stemmed from earlier research into the chemical process for aluminium, which used sodium. This had been developed by St. Claire-Deville in France as far back as 1854, but the cost of metallic sodium kept the price high. Castner developed a cheaper chemical process for sodium, but found that the new electrolytic reduction of aluminum had made the whole business obsolete[16]). The latter process was developed simultaneously and independently by Hall in the United States and Héroult in France, and patented in 1886. The aluminum industry grew rapidly with sharply falling prices, and tended to separate from the chemical industry. The other use of electrolysis in metallurgy, which antedates the aluminum process, and even the electrical industry itself, is electroplating, and the more general process of depositing pure metals from solution. Indeed, the first dynamo designed by Siemens was for refining copper.

The other metallurgical processes involving electricity are electrothermal rather than electrolytic. They are based on the possibility of achieving high temperatures in an electric furnace, far higher than with other fuels. This is done either with an electric arc, as in Moissan's furnace of 1892, or by passing a current through the mass to be heated. A number of products were made in this manner after 1890, the chief ones being calcium carbide, silicon carbide and other abrasives, ferro-alloys, phosphorus, and graphite electrodes. The most important product at one time seemed to be calcium carbide, which is both a source of nitrogen for fertilizers and explosives, and of acetylene for lighting and chemical syntheses. But synthetic ammonia, petroleum, and electricity largely displaced carbide which was significant only in times of shortages. On the other hand, the various metals and abrasives produced by electric means have become very important in the production and working of alloy steels.

Seen with a half century of hindsight, the chemical industry of 1914 appears modest. Its technology was only beginning to be sophisticated, and its most ambitious efforts were only the forerunners of later developments. Yet even so brief a survey as this has shown that the industry had come of age in many important respects. The industry produced a great variety of products, and sold to many different users. The principles of reliance on scientific research and of the primacy of the technical over the commercial were established, if not always observed. Although the quantitative expression of its potential for growth was as yet unspectacular, the industry could clearly envisage continued progress on the basis of existing attitudes and practices.

Notes

1. L. F. Haber, *The Chemical Industry During the 19th Century* (1958); J. J. Beer, *The Emergence of the German Dye Industry* (1959); D. Landes, Technological Change and Development in Western Europe, 1750–1914, in: M. M. Postan and H. J. Habakkuk, eds., *The Cambridge Economic History of Europe,* VI (1965), pp. 274–585.

2. T. J. Markovitch, L'industrie française de 1789 à 1964; sources et méthodes, *Cahiers de l'ISEA,* AF 4, no. 163 (July 1965), pp. 1–231; W. G. Hoffmann, *Das Wachstum der deutschen Wirtschaft seit der Mitte des 19. Jahrhunderts* (1965).

3. In addition to references in note 1, for France, see: P. Baud, *L'industrie chimique en France* (1932); M. Fauque, *L'évolution économique de la grande industrie chimique en France* (1932); R. Richeux, *L'industrie chimique en France: structure et production, 1850–1957* (1958). For Germany, see: A. Binz, *Ursprung und Entwicklung der chemischen Industrie* (1910); F. Redlich, *Die volkswirtschaftliche Bedeutung der deutschen Teerfarbenindustrie* (1914); H. Schall, *Die chemische Industrie Deutschlands* (1959); C. Ungewitter, *Monographie über die chemische Industrie* (1926); A. Zart, *Die Entwicklung der chemischen Grossindustrie* (1922). For Switzerland, see: R. Baumgartner, *Die wirtschaftliche Bedeutung der chemischen Industrie in Basel* (1923); G. F. Jaubert, *Historique de l'industrie suisse des matières colorantes artificielles* (1896); also the excellent company histories of the Swiss firms Geigy, Sandoz, and CIBA (see the Bibliography).

4. The important sources for this section, including the schematic figures, are: P. Baud, *Chimie industrielle,* 2nd ed. (1927); G. Lunge, *Coal, Tar and Ammonia,* 5th ed. (1916); R. Shreve, *The Chemical Process Industries* (1945); T. Thorpe, *Dictionary of Applied Chemistry,* 4th ed. (1937); and C. Singer, ed., *A History of Technology* (1957–58), especially vol. 4, ch. 8, and vol. 5, ch. 11. This last work emphasizes British developments rather heavily.

5. See, in addition to the sources in note 4, Koppers, *Ein halbes Jahrhundert im Dienste der Kohleveredelung* (1951).

6. In fact, Laurent of Lyons had synthesized picric acid from phenol in 1842, and this was used as a dye. But this and a few others remained isolated developments, whereas Perkin's discovery opened up a vast new field.

Full bibliographical data are given in the Bibliography at the end of the book.

7. Though A. W. Hoffman, who supervised Perkin and other early English workers, returned to his native Germany around 1862.
8. E. Fleurent, *Les industries chimiques et la production générale en France* (1920), p. 40.
9. *Ibid.*, pp. 37, 137. Also M. Lambert, Les engrais chimiques et les produits chimiques utiles à l'agriculture, in: Association Nationale d'Expansion Economique, *Enquête sur la production française et la concurrence étrangère* (1917), pp. 19, 27.
10. The forerunners of the ammonia synthesis, insofar as processes involving sophisticated engineering are concerned, were the two sulfuric acid processes and the Solvay process. However, in this case, the use of gases and the severe conditions of operation gave rise to problems of a different order of magnitude.
11. See K. Holdermann, *Im Banne der Chemie: Carl Bosch, Leben und Werk* (1960); A. Mittasch, *Geschichte der Ammoniaksynthese* (1951).
12. K. Holdermann, pp. 139–42.
13. L. F. Haber, p. 107.
14. See F. S. Taylor, *A History of Industrial Chemistry* (1957), pp. 383–396; P. Ferchland, Die elektrochemische Industrie Deutschlands, *Monographien über angewandte Elektrochemie*, vol. XII (1904); V. Barut, *L'industrie de l'électrochimie et de l'électrométallurgie en France* (1924).
15. The classification is not an exact one, since metallurgical processes fall into one of the two other categories, and the production of sodium and potassium is more chemical than metallurgical, though both substances are metals.
16. Castner turned to cyanides and the problem of gold recovery in an effort to market the now redundant sodium. The demand was so great that the electrolytic process was developed to meet it. The company in which Castner developed this flourishing business was still called the Aluminium Company, though it scarcely even got started in this line.

2

The chemical industry in three European countries: comparative performance and the role of market factors

1. The industry in France, Germany, and Switzerland, 1850–1914

1.1. France

Until 1850 France was second only to Britain in the production of industrial chemicals, which meant essentially the Leblanc soda process and the related chamber process for sulfuric acid, as well as a number of inorganic specialty products. The heavy chemical industry continued to be important throughout the second half of the 19th century, even though the technology either remained stable, as in the case of sulfuric acid, or was developed outside France, as in the case of the ammonia–soda process and most of the modifications in the Leblanc process introduced in the fight for survival after 1875. There was considerable quantitative growth in these traditional lines, and the production of superphosphate fertilizers ensured an ample market for acid after 1870. But this was a stable, if reasonably prosperous industry, with slow technical change and virtually no research.

Another important area was that of specialties, centered in Lyons. A great many products with varied uses were made, and there was frequent innovation on an empirical basis. The firms were smaller than in the area of heavy chemicals, though even there the French firms were smaller than the British. There was a tendency to diversification into specialties among the established companies such as Kuhlmann, St. Gobain, and Péchiney, to supplement their main activity in the soda-acid field, where profit margins were often low.

France also took an active part in the beginnings of the organic chemical industry, but activity was brutally cut off in 1863 by the famous *affaire La Fuchsine*, and by 1870 France no longer mattered as a producer of organic dyes[1]).

In brief, La Fuchsine was a company founded in Lyons in 1863 to make and sell the first synthetic dye discovered in France, Verguin's fuchsine. In fact the company was organized not to carry out chemical research and manufacture, but to exploit a monopoly granted the owners of the patent for the dye. Under the French law of 1844 the inventor of a new product had a monopoly right to make and sell it. The Company, founded with the aid of a large amount of capital from the newly created Crédit Lyonnais bank, devoted its energies to preventing the manufacture of fuchsine by others, who developed new and better processes and especially other dyes derived from fuchsine. The courts held that the patent covered fuchsine, however made, and also other materials for which fuchsine was an intermediate. La Fuchsine soon began to lose money as dyes were smuggled into France, and by 1868 the technical men and manufacturers had left the business, leaving the financiers to liquidate it.

The consequences of the affair were drastic indeed, with respect to France's role in the new industry. One is tempted to conclude that 'it is impossible to exaggerate the importance' of this incident, though the story seems suspiciously simple, as will be discussed below. At any rate, a number of French chemists who had begun to work on the new dyes left the country, many for Switzerland, and only one firm remained in this field in France. This was Poirrier & Dalsace, later the *Compagnie des Matières Colorantes de Saint Denis*, which bought the assets of La Fuchsine. Later, Swiss and German firms established dyestuff works in France, largely tariff factories that performed only simple finishing operations on imported intermediaries. As will be shown later, more was involved for France than a debit in the balance of payments, though the full effects of the lag in organic chemicals were not made apparent until the advent of World War I.

By 1900 or a little before, it had become a commonplace that France was backward in chemical research and especially in production. The critical chorus, in France and outside, became louder still at the beginning of the World War, when German imports were cut off[2]). As so often happens, the French technical lag had in fact become something of a myth just when it was acknowledged and held to be all but irreversible. To be sure, Germany led in the now traditional organic synthesis industries, in nitrogenous fertilizers, and in chemical production generally, just as she led France in most branches of heavy or medium industry. Furthermore, Germany's greatest chemical triumphs in the development of synthetics were yet to come, from the Haber–Bosch process of 1913 to synthetic gasoline and rubber in the interwar period. But in the new chemical industries that sprang up between 1895 and 1913 – such as electrochemistry and metallurgy, compressed gases, artificial fibers, and the early plastics – France's role in innovation and production was honorable. In addition, the French industry was able to make up its qualitative lag and a large part of its quantitative lag as well, when the war removed German competition and created a huge demand for organic chemicals for munitions. The reason for this need not be sought only in the tonic effects of war effort on efficiency. By 1914 a large part of Germany's stock of technical knowledge was the common property of technical men everywhere. Experience, organization, and scale made it difficult for the industry to get a foothold in France. The German firms could have undersold the French even without dumping, but would not have hesitated to use that tactic if necessary. Yet despite these influences, there was in the prewar period increased activity in organic production in France, notably in the group of firms which later united to form Rhone–Poulenc, now the largest group of manufacturing firms in France[3]). When the war came, France pooled technical knowledge and manpower, and soon was able to produce a variety of intermediate and other organics in large quantities. It would be perhaps excessive to suggest that success in one branch, organic synthesis, made the Germans less aware of opportunities elsewhere, but it is certain that in those areas of chemical production where physical chemistry provided the scientific base, Germany had nothing like the hegemony she had acquired in dyestuffs and other organic chemicals.

Preliminary data from Markovitch's work on French industrial growth give indications of the size and growth of the industry[4]). Production appears to have grown more slowly than for factory industry as a whole until the 1880's, and more quickly thereafter, but the industry continued to represent about 2% of total French industry, or 4% to 6% of the total excluding construction, clothing, food processing, and woodworking. Annual growth rates for chemicals were between 2% and 3% for the decades between 1845–54 and 1875–85, and then rose to 4.4% to 5.5% until 1913. In foreign trade, using a restricted definition of chemicals, 1913 exports were valued at 238 million francs, or 2.9% of visible exports[5]). It must be stressed that the numbers represent orders of magnitude, particularly as output data tend to be restricted to a few commodities, rather than being based on sales of firms.

1.2. Germany

The German chemical industry was a showcase within a showcase so far as economic growth in the latter part of the 19th century is concerned. In 1860 Germany had almost no large-scale chemical industry, though some acid and soda, as well as a variety of special products, were made. The first significant ventures were in the area of synthetic dyestuffs from coal-tar, in contrast to France (and Britain), where the first sizeable firms produced heavy chemicals. The organic manufacturers, who soon diversified and integrated their operations, came to dominate the world market for dyes, displacing the early British and French, even though these countries continued to be among the leading consumers. Several of these firms grew to be very large indeed for this industry, the best known and largest being the BASF, Bayer, and Höchst[6]). In 1904 began a series of mergers and agreements which culminated in the formation, in 1925, of the chemical trust known as IG-Farben, AG.

The dyestuff manufacturers made synthetic drugs after about 1890, and in addition there were important firms specializing in drugs and other fine chemicals, in particular Merck of Darmstadt. There were also firms in the areas of specialties, electrochemicals (after 1890), and of course, heavy chemicals. Demand for inorganic materials came from within the chemical industry in Germany to a much greater extent than in France or Britain, where end-uses in textiles, glass, soap, and fertilizer predominated. There was downward pressure on the prices of heavy chemicals in Germany, since the main users were also potential (and in some cases actual) suppliers.

Germany did not go through the struggle between the Leblanc and Solvay processes to any extent. Until the 1870s most soda was imported from Britain. When a tariff was put on this material, so that Germany could expand her production, there was no question of installing any but Solvay plants. We have seen that the production of fertilizers became an important industry, as agriculture rapidly expanded its consumption of these materials (only in phosphates did French production exceed German). The Stassfurt deposits supplied potash to all Europe, and Germany imported huge quantities of Chilean nitrates. In 1913 it was estimated that Germany used at least 600 000 tons of nitrates per year on her soil, as well as 460 000 tons of ammonium sulfate derived from coal-tar distillation[7]). This last industry was an important one since it supplied the raw materials for the organic industry, as well as for fertilizer. Germany depended up to the 1880s on British tar from gas works, but the development of by-product coking in Germany solved this problem. The last autarkic statement may be poor economics, but it reflects a driving force for innovation in the German chemical industry, namely national self-sufficiency in commodities, especially raw materials.

W. G. Hoffmann's recent work on the quantitative aspects of German growth since 1850 yields a number of indices of growth and relative size for the chemical industry[8]). The production data unfortunately refer only to four commodities up to 1908, and two of these (soap and rubber) fall

Table 2. Summary of data concerning the German chemical industry.

(a) Growth rates (annual)

		(%)	Source ref. p.
1872–1913	Chemical production	6.2	63
	All industrial production (including crafts)	3.7	
1850–1913	Employment in chemicals	4.0	68
	Industrial employment	1.9	
1875–1913	Labor productivity, chemicals	2.3	69
	Labor productivity all industry	1.6	

(b) Characteristics of the chemical industry as a percentage of all industry, selected years

	1875	1895	1907	Source ref. p.
Employment	1.3	1.9	2.2	68
		(1891–1900)	(1901–1910)	
Machinery (HP) (industry includes mining)	2.2	3.0	3.1	79
Paid-in corporate capital (including mining & transport)	3.6 (1876)	6.1	4.7	772–73
Bonds in circulation (including mining & transport)	6.2 (1882)	3.3	2.9	778–79

Source: W. G. Hoffmann, *Das Wachstum der deutschen Wirtschaft seit der Mitte des 19. Jahrhunderts* (1965).

outside the scope of the present study. Table 2 summarizes the known data, although a variety of definitional and statistical problems make it difficult to regard them as more than illustrative of orders of magnitude. The picture that emerges confirms the impression of rapid (and steady) growth and presents few surprises. It is normal to find the chemical industry holding a more substantial place in measures of capital than of labor, since the denominators include such industries as leather and woodworking, clothing, and food processing, which were not highly mechanized but employed a large share of the industrial labor force. The comparatively modest rate of growth of labor productivity is probably the result of inadequate output statistics.

This survey of the German industry has been brief, not because the subject matter is thus exhausted or the data are particularly scanty, but to some extent because 'les peuples heureux n'ont pas d'histoire'. Also, the spectacular story of the giant dye works has overshadowed the history of other, more modest branches of the industry, just as the 'affaire La Fuchsine' has obscured continuing activity in France.

1.3. Switzerland

The chemical industry of Switzerland resembled that of Germany, though of course on a smaller scale. Perhaps it resembled even more the stereotype of the German industry as one dominated by a few large dyestuff producers engaged heavily in research than it did that industry itself. In Switzerland it was very nearly accurate to limit the industry to the three or four dyestuff houses of Basle, whereas this was less legitimate for the German 'big three' of Ludwigshafen, Leverkusen, and Höchst.

Until 1860 there was a small soda-acid industry in the Zurich area, where there were textile customers and some limited natural resources. This activity did not lead to any later development, and, if anything, tended to diminish absolutely as it became easier to transport chemicals. The rise of the Swiss chemical industry can in fact be traced directly to the beginning of dyestuff manufacture, and in particular to the debacle associated with the fuchsine case in France. Every one of the Basle firms traces its existence as a chemical firm to French emigrants. The interconnections are shown in Fig. 4.

From the first, the dye manufacturers relied on foreign markets and on imports of materials to a considerable extent, which in part explains the

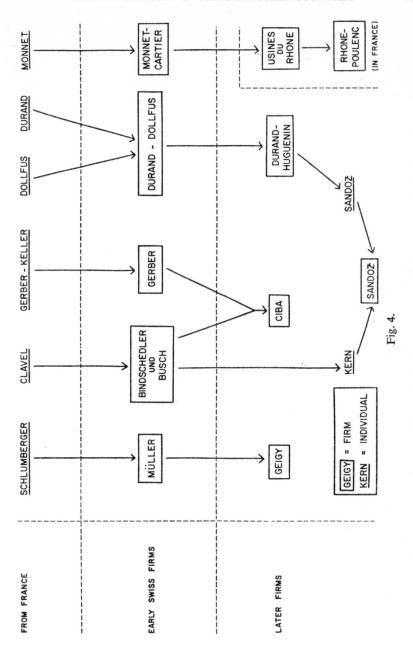

Fig. 4.

location of the industry in Basle and, for a time, in Geneva. Under the pressure of German competition, the Basle firms were forced to specialize in expensive and technically difficult products, though they could invade other markets if cartel arrangements led to exceptional profit opportunities[9]. Raw materials and intermediates were imported from Germany, and there was frequent change in products as existing processes became easier to work and the Swiss lost their advantage. From dyestuffs, production expanded into pharmaceuticals, agricultural chemicals, and other specialties. Exports accounted for the vast majority of production, and tariff factories were established in various countries after about 1882. In 1895, out of an estimated world production of dyestuffs of 122 to 125 million francs, Switzerland had 16 million, about as much as all others exept Germany[10]. This understates the importance of the two main producers, since it does not take into account ownership of foreign plants. The ratio of the Basle to the German dyestuffs industry was about $1:5\frac{1}{2}$ in value terms and $1:18$ in terms of manpower.

2. The role of factor supply and product demand

The discussion will again abandon the division by countries and consider the role of inputs and demand. It is perhaps worth summarizing the main features of the three industries which must be accounted for in any explanation. In France: (1) satisfactory development of the heavy chemicals sector and of the specialties industry, at least in quantitative terms; (2) a sort of technical eclipse from about 1860 to 1895; (3) poor performance in the area of organic chemicals and fertilizers, except for phosphates; (4) a revival after 1895, particularly in new sectors. In Germany: (1) rapid development of the industry from 1860, with emphasis on organic chemicals; (2) quantitatively strong performance of the inorganic branch, largely auxiliary to the leading organic sector; (3) rapid progress in fertilizers, culminating in the development of the synthetic ammonia process. In Switzerland: the same pattern as Germany (except for fertilizers), only more accentuated, with concentration on highly elaborated organic products, and reliance on imports for cheaper materials such as inorganics and intermediate products. The order of factors is somewhat arbitrary.

2.1. Resources

The chemical industry is quite resource-intensive, in the sense that the cost of materials, including water and energy, is an important fraction of total cost, especially of direct or 'prime' cost. This was even more true in the 19th century than it is now, and most true in the heavier branches of the industry. Therefore, with given technology, natural resources can be expected to account for a large part of the problems and achievements of the industry. And indeed they have often been made to do so. For example, St. Gobain stressed the importance of the Sain-Bel pyrites deposits, both in weighing a merger with a producer of sulfuric acid, Perret, in 1869, and in evaluating the prospects of the company in chemicals in 1882[11]). The high cost of French coal was monotonously put forward in explanation of the lower efficiency of the country's industry, in chemicals as elsewhere.

The question remains as to whether this resource problem was an explanation or an excuse. There is probably something to the coal problem, especially in connection with transport and markets. The role of transport will be examined later, but it can be said now that France's coal deposits were not well located from the point of view of the chemical industry, except in the North. And this area was vulnerable to foreign producers with even better resource bases, owing to low transport costs. Conversely, the Rhine provided a favorable location for both the Swiss and the German industries, and not only from the point of view of transport, important as this was. It provided the two most important resources for much of the industry, coal and water, the latter especially important as a raw material, a utility (power, steam, cooling), and a receptacle for the ever-troublesome waste products[12]).

Nevertheless, it would be wrong to ascribe major importance to resources in explaining the French lag or the success of the other two countries. The reason is to be sought in the qualifying phrase above, 'with given technology'. Here, *ceteris* are emphatically not *paribus*. The whole history of the industry, (and our criterion of its success and contribution to growth), is change in technology. And it is most often in response to resource problems that changes took place. Indeed, the nature of the chemical industry is that it uses the transformation of matter to save resources, to increase the value of existing ones, or to create resources where none were before. This process antedates the age of synthetics. The early heavy chemicals industry was resource-saving. Soda replaced barilla, kelp, and plant ashes in soap, glass, and textiles, while chlorine bleaches freed agricultural resources, replacing sunlit grass and sour milk in bleaching cloth[13]). The development of the pyrites mine at Sain-Bel, so important to St. Gobain in later years, was a direct result of a sulfur shortage brought on by a monopoly position in the Sicilian mines. In the later period examples are numerous. German research increased the usefulness of energy sources such as brown coal, recovered metals from pyrites used to make acid, and synthesized most of the materials which the country had to import, this last only partly in the period under study. During World War I, German industry even was able to dispense with pyrites and extract sulfur economically from commonly available gypsum[14]).

The French industry, on the other hand, was often unwilling to change the existing technology in order to take advantage of limited or imperfect resources. Existing coal producers, owners of timber, madder growers, or the government salt monopoly were to be protected rather than replaced by more efficient processes, with the tariff as the first line of defense. On this showing, it can almost be claimed that good resources acted as a brake on technical progress, and therefore on the chemical industry. Poor resources forced the Swiss to specialize in the one way not subject to adverse effects from changing technology, namely incorporating the latest techniques in their products, and abandoning those productions in which increments of technical effort no longer yielded enough net return to offset higher material costs.

Thus, although resources provided certain advantages to particular sectors, such as the German potash industry or the French applications of hydroelectricity, the chemical industry provides a good example both of resources as an endogenous factor in growth and of the stimulus of inadequate supplies of raw materials. It was technical progress which made resources out of previously unnoticed materials, such as pyrites, brown coal, bauxite, and phosphate rock. And the stimulus to progress came more often from pressure on the supply of natural products to chemical and other industries than from a desire to make better use of known reserves.

2.2. Labor

Labor played a minor role in the development of the chemical industry, not counting of course technically trained manpower, which is a separate input[15]). Little labor was used and much of this was unskilled. The exceptions were chiefly workers in the building and metal trades who were employed in constructing and maintaining chemical plants and equipment. Such operating labor as was needed was readily available at low wages, and consisted mainly of adult males. Conditions of work were poor even by the standards of the day, and foreign labor was common in Basle and Marseilles and elsewhere. Unionization was not widespread. The concentration of the industry in some rural or sparsely settled areas, and the health hazards, made social services significant, as well as necessary, rather early.

It has been surmised that the character of German workers, disciplined but lacking in initiative, was especially suited to an industry without the traditional craft skills and where technical standards rather than human judgement, determined the actions of workers, but this hardly seems a major factor.

2.3. Capital

It is a commonplace to speak of the chemical industry as capital-intensive. This is true if one considers the ratio of capital to labor, but not necessarily with respect to output. And the importance of reproducible capital was certainly less in the 19th century than it is in the 20th[16]). There is no question that most chemical firms grew with little or no recourse to long-term capital markets, at least in their early stages. Such effects as the market for funds may have had, must be of secondary importance.

A study by V. Muthesius in Bäumler's history of the Höchst Company provides useful evidence on the financial conditions facing the German firms during their rapid growth[17]). Höchst was founded with an initial capital of about 111 000 marks, which grew in eight years to 1.45 million marks (1870), and to 8.5 million by 1880. The latter sum represented the value of the owners' contribution to the *Aktiengesellschaft* founded in that year. Up to 1880 there had been, insofar as can be judged, no recourse to external financing, but the firm planned to initiate a series of expansions, beginning with an acid plant, and felt that continued autofinancing was impracticable. Two aspects of the early years following incorporation are worth noting. The first is that the two banks which handled the issue of shares and later their introduction on the stock exchange were local Frankfurt houses rather than large industrial banks. The other is that Höchst went public during a financial crisis, so that the company financed its expansion for the next few years largely with short-term bank credits plus retained earnings. Sale of shares brought in 1.5 million in 1881 and 2 million (40% of a nominal capital increase of 5 million) in 1882.

Yet there is a plausible reason for examining the role of capital in tracing the development of the industry in the three countries. It is known that Basle and Germany had unusually favorable conditions as regards the supply of industrial capital, whereas French industry typically found it difficult to raise long-term funds[18]. The traditional role of Basle as a gathering place for funds in search of safety from political turbulence is well known, as is the role of industrial banks in the industrialization of Germany[19]. In France, there is the remarkable story of La Fuchsine and the Crédit Lyonnais, the only example I know of direct participation by a major bank in the launching of a chemical venture (see above). Here capital did play a major role, but hardly a positive one! From that time onward especially, the great French banks showed scarcely any interest in the chemical industry[20]. The question remains as to whether the industry was not equally indifferent, but spotty evidence indicates that regional banks played a role in financing chemical firms[21]. This makes it possible to speculate that the industry, and perhaps French industry in general, would have benefited from greater strength in this part of the financial market, and from active local and regional banks in all the regions of France. It is impossible to go beyond such speculation, although one may nourish it with the observation that the regions with strong banks, such as Lorraine, the North, and Lyons–Savoie–Dauphiné, were active chemical regions.

In Germany, where industrial banks were so active in financing industrialization, it is difficult to find any considerable role for them in the chemical industry. The early ventures were financed with merchant capital (Bayer and Höchst, for example), or with the aid of local finance (the BASF), and grew by reinvesting profits. A study of the great German banks in 1905 shows relatively little participation in the chemical industry[22]. In Basle there were also close relations between bankers and manufacturers, but it is hard to say whether these went much beyond routine commercial operations[23].

For want of data, any conclusions must remain tentative. In the period before World War I chemical ventures began on a small scale, either as extensions of an existing business, such as dyeing, trade in dyes and drugs and the like, or with local backing. Expansion may have been facilitated in Germany and Switzerland by more readily available capital, but there is no record of French firms unable to expand for want of funds. Certainly there was no large-scale recourse to equity financing, in any of the countries, nor were the firms heavily burdened with long-term debt. Finally, it may be that German capital was more willing to enter industries where profits had to await long gestation as technology was developed than was the case in France or Britain, where more immediate gain was sought, abroad if there seemed to be insufficient domestic opportunities. Yet the large German firms paid extraordinary dividends, at least computed on the original cost of the shares, over 20% as a whole for every year between 1890 and 1903[24]).

2.4. Demand

In its early stages the chemical industry was created and conditioned largely by demand. It began as an adjunct of the early large-scale industries, such as textiles, soap, and glass, which found that they needed larger amounts of auxiliary materials of a kind not available from mines, quarries, and fields. The location of the early works was often determined by that of the user, in part because chemicals were difficult to transport and store. Later, when the chemical works produced for a larger market and on a different scale, their location was more often determined by resources and transport, as well as water and the vexing problems of waste disposal. However, in France especially, chemical firms did not always forsake urban areas, convenient from the point of view of labor and of waste products (such as bones, sewage, etc.) which served as raw materials. The locational shift towards concern with production costs was paralleled by an economic one, and demand ceased to be the driving force for growth and change in the industry. In fact, demand factors sometimes worked against the industry, with an inelastic schedule due to inertia on the part of customers. Again, these influences were most noticeable in France.

So long as chemicals were an auxiliary industry, demand was inelastic. When the industry outgrew local markets it first expanded into new geographical markets, and then into new uses. This meant replacing existing suppliers, older products, and sometimes traditional methods and whole technologies. In the first case, that of displacing other suppliers or identical natural products, demand was elastic, and growth was the result of lower costs. Where expansion required changes in the technology of the user industry, or at least in the habits of the user, one cannot speak of elasticity of demand at all in the static sense. The chemical manufacturer had to develop the new techniques, to the extent that innovation was not forthcoming in the user industry, and convince potential customers to apply the changes. This problem will be discussed in more detail in Chapter 6 but the fact that chemicals were sold in large part to traditional and established industries made this innovating role important. Moreover, much change in the chemical industry was the result of the search for new processes in the manufacture of existing products. Here, too, the stimulus came from supply rather than demand.

Demand could hurt the industry where the new methods it was introducing along with its products reduced the advantage enjoyed by the user industry under the old technology, and were therefore resisted, or where there was strong, presumably irrational, resistance to change on the part of customers. This last was the case in French agriculture, which would not make extensive use of chemical fertilizers except in the north and north-central regions of France. The reasons for this have never been completely studied, at least not to my knowledge, and the role of the chemical industry as supplier is at most a partial one. The predominance of small free- or leaseholds was certainly a factor. Probably the main reason was that the use of fertilizers required greater changes in methods and management than farmers could or would make, especially in the matter of willingness to increase purchased inputs. Scarcity of capital combined here with high liquidity preference. On the side of supply, neither the industry nor the government did much to systematize the technology of fertilizer use, to spread reliable and useful information, or to regulate the trade in chemical and other fertilizers, where fraud and quackery often increased and justified the farmer's 'méfiance'[25]). Table 3 gives the comparative use of chemical fertilizers per hectare in France, Germany, and Belgium.

An illustration of the case of poor demand due to reluctance to abandon a specialized technology can also be found in France, in the field of synthetic dyes. French dyers, especially in the Lyons silk industry, stood to lose if their complex and secret empirical technology was made obsolete by new dyes, such as fuchsine. Similarly, new piece-dyeing methods hurt the skilled Lyons weavers or 'canuts'. This has been adduced in ex-

Table 3.   Use of chemical fertilizers around 1914 in France, Germany, Belgium (kg/hectare/yr).

	France	Germany	Belgium
Total	57.6	168	274
Phosphates	52	80	140
Potash	3.2	10	5
Nitrogen	2.4	23	72

Source: E. Fleurent, *Les industries chimiques et la production générale en France*, p. 137.

planation of the behavior of Renard, the manufacturer of fuchsine, who considered the new dye a temporary fad, and a source of windfall profits, rather than the beginning of a revolution in his trade[26]). Thus dyers and madder growers were allies in discouraging the new synthetic dye industry. When true substitutes for natural dyes were made, after 1869, French demand was and remained substantial, but it was filled by imports or products from tariff factories.

In Switzerland there was less commitment to the old dyeing techniques, and from the first the new materials were exported rather than used locally. The same was true of Germany, where dyers played even a lesser role in the development of the chemical industry. And in both, the demand for inorganic chemicals was strengthened by the growth in organics, which are great users of heavy chemicals.

The level of demand for established products depended of course on the general rate of growth of industrial production, and this was higher in Germany than in France. Nonetheless, the German industry depended much less on its home market than the French. Export orientation was, of course, characteristic of German industry as a whole, and this perhaps accounts for the more elastic demand faced even at home by the German producers. French industrialists seemed to accept higher costs of chemicals as well as other inputs as part of their normal conditions of doing business, the remedy for both suppliers and buyers being protection. Debates and hearings on commercial policy are enlightening in this regard. In discussions of the reasons for higher French industrial costs, chemicals were only mentioned by other chemical producers, and cloth printers[27]). Whether this was because of the minor role chemicals played in the total cost of textiles (aside from dyeing and printing) or because of inaccurate costing, it is hard to say. The textile manufacturers did not challenge the call for protection on the part of chemical firms, since they led the fight for high tariffs themselves. The key point is, of course, not that greater efficiency gave the German industry a great comparative advantage, but that incentives for would-be exporters to lower costs were a driving force for technical effort and continuing progress. Nevertheless, demand was only permissive. Britain exported chemicals, especially soda, and the combination of scale and the need to remain competitive spurred cost reduction. But inadequate technical effort limited the scope of possible improvements.

One instance when demand favored rapid growth in chemicals was in the initial establishment of dyestuff manufacture in Basle and in the Rhineland. Demand for fuchsine was buoyant, owing largely to the dictates of fashion at the French Imperial court, and the monopoly shut off most supply from inside France. But Basle was admirably suited to supply France even without sanction by the law, and much of the early production was smuggled from there or across the Rhine into France. Later development did not benefit from ready demand, and markets had to be won by means of application research and aggressive selling.

Demand was all-important at the beginning of the history of industrial chemistry, and again in the initial stages of the organic industry. But further growth depended on innovation in supply, the result either of cheaper processes or of new products or applications developed and introduced largely by the chemical industry itself, and even sometimes forced on reluctant users.

2.5. Transport

The role of transport in determining the location and the costs of chemical production has been emphasized by all treatments of the subject. In the industry's early phases, when small quantities were involved and the processes not perfected, the transport of raw materials and utilities was less of a problem than that of finished products, so that plants located near the market. Raw materials were rather easily available in the limited quantities required. Thus southeastern France, with numerous small coal deposits, or the Zurich area, with some salt and limestone, were early centers of the soda industry. Greater scale, more complex manufacture, and improvements in product handling changed the emphasis, not away from transport, but to cheap transport of bulky raw materials and intermediate products[28]). Water transport proved especially useful, and this, combined with the huge demand for water as a raw material and a utility, made navigable rivers and harbors the natural location for many chemical plants, especially large ones.

In the matter of transport, France was less favorably situated than the other countries. The southeast had few navigable rivers, the Rhône being only partly usable, and it had poor connections with the north and east, important markets for chemicals. The west, which had fertilizer markets and ports to handle imports of these materials, was even more poorly provided with waterways[29]). The north and east were better in this respect, and more chemical production came to be concentrated in the north and Lorraine. Here, however, French producers had little advantage over their Belgian, British, or German competitors, and differences in the cost of coal or a higher salt tax could open the market to imports of heavy chemicals. In early 1870, St. Gobain[30]) favored a merger with Perret of Lyons, among other reasons because they did not wish to rely on markets to the north and east exclusively, these being too open to foreigners. Problems of transport also limited the development of the electrochemical industry in the dead-end valleys of the Alps[31]).

In addition to natural disadvantages in transport, France also had problems due to insufficiencies in railroads and canals. It was claimed that one reason for the difficulties in the post-1860 period was insufficient development of social overhead capital, meaning chiefly waterways[32]). The chemical industry in particular complained frequently that railroads discriminated against chemical products, lumping them indiscriminately in high-rate categories as dangerous products[33]). The chemical industries were too small to have much bargaining power with the railroads, and, except in special cases such as the Alpine valleys, were not an important factor in the demand for transport, except locally. The combination of technical inertia and dirigism which characterized much of government action in France, extended to the railroad bureaucracy.

In Germany and Switzerland the transport factor was indeed significant, but it can be almost summed up in a word, the Rhine. Until electrochemicals began to be developed, most of Germany's chemical industry was either on the Rhine or on its tributaries. Berlin and Hamburg were the only significant exceptions, and they had access to water transport as well. Very early, Mannheim displaced Stuttgart as a center of chemical production for this reason[34]). Basle came to be the only significant chemical center in Switzerland because of the transport advantages afforded by the Rhine[35]), while the ventures in Geneva and Zurich failed to grow. Again, electrochemicals were the exception to this rule, along with a number of small firms in inorganic chemicals and specialties which cause the employment statistics to underestimate the role of Basle[36]). It is necessary to remember, however, that Basle's location presented an opportunity only to the extent that the industry there was technologically dynamic enough to face exposure to the powerful competitors down the Rhine on whom it also relied for many material inputs. Communication is a two-way street, and the parallel with northern and eastern France, where easy transport was seen as largely an open door for competitive imports, is illuminating. In the one case where ease of transport delayed the development of an industry, namely German soda which could not compete with the British until a tariff was established, the delay was salutory. When the tariff was put on, in 1879, the industry applied the modern Solvay process, and escaped being saddled with large obsolescent Leblanc plants, which persisted in France and Britain.

3. Conclusion

Differences in market conditions contribute little to an analysis of the relative performance of the chemical industries of France, Germany, and Switzerland. This is not to argue that better supplies of coal, more efficient water transport, more daring customers, or better regional and industrial banks would not have led to better performance in France. They probably would have. The point is that the more successful German and Swiss industries either relied little on their more advantageous situation, or, through technical dynamism, were able to grasp the opportunities afforded by free trade and low transport costs and create advantageous market positions.

The case against factor supplies and markets as the key to the industry's growth is strengthened by looking for a moment at Britain. Here was the unchallenged industrial leader, with an excellent economic climate and many advantages for chemical production. Resources were abundant, transport highly developed, and capital freely available despite the absence of industrial banks. Labor may have been dearer than on the continent, but chemical production made few demands on the labor market. Chemical production was, in fact, highly developed[37]. Britain dominated the world market for soda and related chemicals and was nearly the sole supplier of coal-tar until 1880. Even with respect to organic chemicals, Britain was the early leader. Perkin was the first to invent a successful synthetic dye, nor did he fail to begin manufacture. Finally, Britain was and remained by far the largest market for chemicals, in particular dyestuffs. Well into the 1860s, young Germans interested in chemical production or applications had to complete their formal education by a stay in one or more English works. Caro, later of the BASF, for example, lived in Manchester for some seven years, and his circle there included several future leaders of the German industry, as well as Friedrich Engels[38].

The early 1860s represented the chemical climacteric for Britain. The Germans, teachers and journeymen, left for home, and the industry lost its technical momentum. The large sectors supplying heavy chemicals and tar began to lose ground owing to competition from the Solvay process and by-product coking soon afterward, and no sizeable new productions emerged.

If growth in the chemical industry was not conditioned primarily by market factors, there remains technical progress, the autonomous push from the side of supply. In analyzing the factors affecting the rate of technical progress, one finds that existing production theory tends to treat it as largely exogenous, that is to do no more than acknowledge its existence. On the macroeconomic level, much work has been done in the direction of measuring change in productivity and assigning some part of it to improvements in the quality of labor through education and training, and the like. For the purposes of this study it is necessary to have a more explicit model of the relationship between economic behavior and technical change in the firm. To this task we now turn.

Notes

1. On La Fuchsine, see especially: J. Bouvier, *Le Crédit Lyonnais de 1863 à 1882* (1961), pp. 374–381; M. Laferrère, *Lyon, ville industrielle* (1960), pp. 155–161; N. Jaquet, *Die Entwicklung und volkswirtschaftliche Bedeutung der schweizerischen*

Full bibliographical data are given in the Bibliography at the end of the book.

Teerfarbenindustrie (1923), pp. 17–25; E. A. Sack, La Fuchsine est centenaire, *Revue générale des matières colorantes. Teintes* (December 1958).

2. An important early analysis of France's lag is A. Haller, *L'industrie chimique* (1895), based on his report from the Chicago Fair of 1893. For wartime studies, see *inter alia*, E. and P. Grandmougin, *La réorganisation de l'industrie chimique en France* (1918); E. Fleurent, *Les industries chimiques en France et en Allemagne*, 2 vols. (1915, 1916); and V. K. Löffl, Die chemische Industrie Frankreichs, *Sammlung chemischer und chemischtechnischer Vorträge*, vol. XXIV (1917).

3. *Entreprise* (September 1962), p. 39.

4. T. J. Markovitch, L'industrie française de 1789 à 1964, *Cahiers de l'ISEA*, no. 163 (July 1965), tables 1–6 in Appendix, especially.

5. E. Fleurent (1920), pp. 145–146.

6. Their full names were, respectively: Badische Anilin- und Soda-Fabrik, Ludwigshafen; Farbwerke, vormals Friedrich Bayer, Leverkusen; and Farbwerke vormals Meister, Lucius Brüning, Höchst-am-Main.

7. M. Lambert, in: *Enquête sur la production nationale et la concurrence étrangère* (1917), pp. 19, 34.

8. W. G. Hoffmann, *Das Wachstum der deutschen Wirtschaft* (1965).

9. For example, the Alizarin Convention of 1881 between German and British producers encouraged Bindschedler-und-Busch to resume manufacture of this staple dyestuff, only to abandon it again when the convention collapsed. A. Bürgin, *Geigy, 1758 bis 1939* (1958), p. 128.

10. L. F. Haber, p. 120.

11. St. Gobain, *Rapports du Conseil d'Administration* (ms.). In 1882, the pyrites mine was seen as the true wealth, 'la vraie richesse' of the firm.

12. The consumption of utilities by one of the large chemical complexes such as the BASF in Ludwigshafen is astronomical, at the present time some 1½ million tons of coal a year and 2 million tons of water a *day*. Data from the BASF brochure: *BASF schreibt Geschichte*.

13. L. F. Haber, pp. 5–9.

14. T. J. Kreps, *The Economics of the Sulfuric Acid Industry* (1938), p. 268.

15. See L. F. Haber, ch. 12; A. Matagrin, *L'industrie des produits chimiques et ses travailleurs* (1925).

16. Data on capital stock are particularly scant. One available figure is the insurance (not book) value of plant and machinery, furniture and fittings for the Sandoz Company, one of the three main Basle firms. In 1910, when the company had sales of 4.0 million francs, the physical assets were insured for 0.7 million francs, whereas the wage bill was 0.6 million francs. *Sandoz, 1886–1961* (1961), p. 136.

17. E. Bäumler, *Ein Jahrhundert Chemie* (1963), pp. 361–392.

18. See, for example, La banque et le crédit, in: Association Nationale d'Expansion Economique, *Enquête sur la production française et la concurrence étrangère* (1917). Long-term funds were especially hard to get for small firms in capital-intensive industries (p. 30).

19. For the Swiss case, see A. Bürgin, *Geigy, 1758 bis 1939*, p. 79.

20. A. Matagrin, p. 272.
21. Regional banks are mentioned in connection with the early development of electro-chemistry in the Alps by V. Barut, *L'industrie de l'électrochimie et de l'électrométallurgie en France* (1924), p. 260; also in rayon near Lyons, M. Labasse, *Les capitaux et la région* (1955), p. 489; Kuhlmann was on the original board of the Crédit du Nord, R. Gendarme, *La région du Nord* (1954), p. 184. J. Laloux, *Le rôle des banques locales et régionales du Nord de la France dans le développement industriel et commercial* (1924), p. 123, notes, that local banks in the north of France were more willing to renew paper, and thus to furnish longer-term credit, than were the big banks.
22. E. Depitre, *Le mouvement de concentration dans les banques allemandes* (1905), p. 80, notes that only 8 bankers were listed as being on the board of chemical companies, *versus* 33 in machinery, 46 in electric utilities, and 69 in coal mining. It should be noted that L. F. Haber, p. 172, calls the connection of banks with the chemical industry in Germany 'particularly close', and notes an increase in the recourse to loan capital after 1890 (p. 173). At least it can be said that the industry was not controlled or launched by the industrial banks.
23. Relations between chemical companies and banks were also noted in France. A. Fisch, *Les industries chimiques de la région lyonnaise* (1923), pp. 78–79, notes connections between Péchiney and the Crédit Lyonnais, Gerland and the same bank, the Société de L'Aluminium and the Société Générale, etc. Again, these dealings probably involved largely commercial short-term loans, or limited expansion of established businesses.
24. L. F. Haber, p. 171.
25. I have been unable to find a satisfactory treatment of this problem, especially in its historical context. The following references cover limited aspects of the question, which continued to dog French agriculture into the middle of the 20th century: Ministère de l'Agriculture, du Commerce et des Travaux Publics, *Enquête sur les engrais industriels* (1865); L. Bargeron, *Le commerce des engrais* (1906); R. Guglielmo, *L'industrie française des engrais chimiques* (1954–56); Quelques aspects du problème des engrais, *Etudes et Conjonctures* (August 1953).
26. See above, p. 35, for a summary of the case and references.
27. See: M. Suilliot, *Réponses au questionnaire du Conseil Supérieur du Commerce et de l'industrie* (1890); *Enquête parlementaire sur le régime économique,* vol. I. *Industries textiles* (1870).
28. In 1855 Henri Merle, the founder of what became Péchiney, stressed the advantages of locating so as to minimize the cost of transporting raw materials. C. J. Gignoux, *Histoire d'une entreprise française* (1955), p. 14.
29. The transport problem may be a partial explanation of the lag in applying chemical fertilizers to agriculture, discussed above. In 1865, it was reported that certain areas in western France gained access to lime for the fields because of roads originally built to repress pro-Bourbon uprisings in 1832. Ministère de l'Agriculture, du Commerce et des Travaux Publics, *Enquête sur les engrais industriels,* p.767.
30. St. Gobain, *Rapports.*

31. R. Blanchard, *La grande industrie chimique dans la France du Sud-Est* (1928), p. 47.

32. *Enquête parlementaire sur le régime économique* I, p. 78.

33. M. Suilliot, pp. 10–11.

34. H. Schall, *Die chemische Industrie Deutschlands* (1959), pp. 26–27.

35. Plus advantages for waste disposal, a serious problem in view of the strict, though reasonable, Swiss authorities. See, in particular: A. Bürgin, pp. 114–117, and P. Koelner, *Aus der Frühzeit der chemischen Industrie Basels* (1937), pp. 121 ff.

36. W. Lehmann, *Die Entwicklung der Standorte der schweizerischen Industrie seit dem Ende des 19. Jahrhunderts* (1952), p. 120.

37. See: L. F. Haber, ch. 9; H. W. Richardson, The Development of the British Dyestuffs Industry before 1939, *Scottish Journal of Political Economy*, IX, 2 (1962), pp. 110–129; L'industrie chimique et la science, Opinion de quelques savants anglais, *Revue de Métallurgie*, XII (August 1915).

38. K. Oberdorffer, ed., *Ludwigshafener Chemiker,* II (1960), pp. 60–62.

3

Growth through technical effort and technical progress

1. A theoretical framework

By assumption and observation, we have narrowed the search for an explanation of growth in the chemical industry to technical change. It is now necessary to consider the mechanism by which firms effect technical progress in their productive operations, and the environmental factors that condition the rate of progress achieved. We shall consider the level of productivity to be a function of knowledge, and explore the implications of discarding the assumption that knowledge is costlessly available to firms in exogenously determined amounts. Instead, economically useful knowledge is considered the product of purposive and resource-using activity. This activity is called *technical effort*. Firms expend technical effort as part of the process of maximizing profits, except that the usual constraint of a fixed and given production-possibility frontier is relaxed.

In order to bring out the way in which technical effort works within the firm, it will be convenient to resort to the time-honored simplification of ideal types. Firms that make substantial use of technical effort, and in which the activity is formalized, will be referred to as *knowledge-centered*. At the other end of the spectrum will be so-called *backward* firms, in which technical effort is minimal and not consciously organized.

1.1. The role and costs of technical effort in the firm

The firm is a unit in which certain resources, or factors of production are brought together according to a given algorithm to produce a particular product or group of products. The algorithm, the recipe for using inputs to produce outputs, is called technology. It is represented in factor space by a series of isoquants, or more generally by a set of points. Each point represents the maximum output obtainable with that mix of inputs (or the minimum of inputs required to produce the stated quantity of output).

$$Q \leqslant f(x_1 \ldots x_n), \tag{1}$$

where Q = output and x_i = one factor of production. Isoquants join all the points with the same value for Q, on the assumption that such points form a continuum. The choice of technique, that is of the point at which production is to be carried out, is then made so as to minimize costs for a particular value of Q and for given prices of x_1 to x_n.

This model of the firm seems both too broad and too restrictive. On the one hand, it assumes complete information about the isoquant map and fully defined and known functions of the form of expression (1) for a wide range of the variables. It also assumes that it is costless to achieve the equality form of (1), or to move from one point on the map to another. On the other hand, it is assumed that the map, the nature of Q, and the list of possible inputs, x_i, are given, and subject only to exogenous change.

For the purposes of this discussion it will be helpful to begin with a more restrictive model of the firm without technical effort, and to argue that technical effort allows the firm not only to behave as the usual model suggests, but also to transcend the restrictions imposed by it. Assume that there is only one output produced in the amount Q using the inputs $x_1 \ldots x_f$ in nearly fixed proportions. The relevant range of factor-space points is limited to a small range about point $\bar{Q}$, plus a similar range at multiples of Q, and perhaps a few points 'far' from $\bar{Q}$. This is illustrated for the case of two inputs by Fig. 5. If there are changes in demand or in factor prices, the firm may move to another point within the range of those defined for it. But moves are not costless, and a small change may not call forth a move, since the expected gain is less than the cost of moving, given the existence, say, of costs sunk in specific factors of production. In particular, the cost of moving depends on how different (i.e., distant) the new point is from $\bar{Q}$ (except for points such as $\bar{Q}_2$ representing additional plants identical to the first, for which the costs of moving may be small). Finally, while at point $\bar{Q}$ the equality form of (1) may hold, a move to a new point will yield, in the short run at least:

$$Q < f(x_1 \ldots x_f). \tag{2}$$

Now a new activity is introduced into the firm, which has for its object the elaboration and implementation of recipes for production. This is

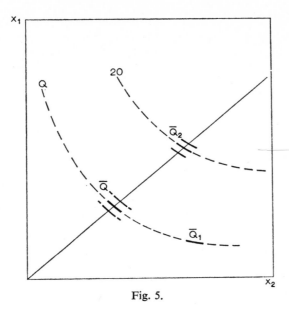

Fig. 5.

technical effort, which uses resources and can be directed, though imperfectly, to solving specific problems. Technical effort will enable the firm to break out of the restrictions of the above model in a variety of ways. The hypothesis put forth here is that all the following 'moves' require technical effort, and that they are therefore similar in kind. Technical effort may achieve the following results:

1. Map out additional points in factor space at which production can be carried out. This allows more complete adjustment to changing factor prices or to a different optimal scale of output.

2. Lower the costs of shifting from one point to another and of achieving maximum output from a given set of inputs.

3. Increase productivity, in the sense of raising the numerical value of maximum output for a given point in factor space.

4. Transform knowledge available from outside into specifically relevant production possibilities. This may involve developing general knowledge into recipes for production, modifying technology used under different conditions elsewhere, or merely acquiring and interpreting information.

5. Develop techniques using different inputs, or resulting in a somewhat modified product.

6. Develop technology in lines not directly related to the firm's original activity. The second part of the book is largely devoted to elaborating on this mechanism.

The point to be stressed is that making available to the firm additional points in 'known' technology is not fundamentally different from maximizing profit on the one hand, and improving technology on the other. All use resources of substantially the same kind, and one cannot even safely predict a ranking of these tasks in terms of the amount of technical effort they are likely to require.

The production and application of knowledge involves costs. Some of these are tangible, such as expenditures on research and development. Others may be intangible, though real. Intangible costs are due to the fact that management's willingness to engage in technical effort is often a limiting factor, and should therefore be thought of as a scarce resource, commanding a rent. The behavioral aspects of technical effort, dealt with in the next section, point to certain qualities of entrepreneurship as being important to understanding growth.

The tangible costs of technical effort involve the expenditure of resources for the production and application of knowledge. In the familiar case of research and development expenditures, the resources consist of fixed capital and, especially, trained manpower or human capital. In addition, the firm engaging in technical effort will incur indirect costs as it adapts production to the requirements of knowledge-centered operation. The productive process must be reorganized to provide information for the research operation, and it must also be flexible enough to accommodate the more frequent and far-reaching change characteristic of knowledge-centered firms. The costs of flexibility were pointed out by Stigler, who argued that firms could choose between more or less sharply curved average cost curves, except that the minimum was higher if average cost varied little with scale (i.e., if marginal cost rose gently in the neighborhood of the minimum cost output)[1]. With technical effort, flexibility extends to more than scale of output, but the same principle of expending resources to increase adaptability holds good. One can think of output and adaptability as joint products, with costs somewhat higher than would be required to produce only physical output under one fixed set of conditions (scale, inputs, input prices, technique)[2].

An alternative way of looking at the role and costs of technical effort is to think of the firm as possessing a stock of knowledge or problem-solving potential that enables it to achieve greater efficiency over time and to be more flexible. The stock earns a rent and, as in the case of capital, depreciates over time. Knowledge is not actually lost, but its economic value decreases as competitive firms acquire the same information, or as new knowledge makes present techniques obsolete. Technical effort is gross investment in the stock of knowledge, partly maintenance and partly providing new opportunities for technical progress.

As portrayed here, technical effort is a necessary part of any firm's activity, and is only in part separable from production itself. Traditionally, it is part of the entrepreneur's job to provide knowledge, to organize the factors of production in an optimum way, to adjust to market changes, and to seek improved methods. Technical effort is thus subsumed under entrepreneurship, and its return is part of entrepreneurial rent. The so-called good entrepreneur carries out these tasks effectively and reaps the corresponding return. However, when technology becomes complex or the firm becomes large, the capacity of the entrepreneur for technical effort is exceeded. It then becomes meaningful to view this activity as one distinct from either management or production, and to distinguish knowledge-centered and backward firms. In the former, the activity becomes formalized, with the expenditure of tangible resources and an organization to transmit information and decisions. In the latter firm, the capacity to transform is limited, and the firm is barely able to cope with externally imposed changes, much less to innovate. Scale and the complexity of techniques lead to the necessary depersonalization of the Schumpeterian engine of growth. Of course, there is still room for variation in the amount and quality of technical effort undertaken, and a box in an organization chart is no guarantee of an effectively functioning unit.

1.2. The extent of technical effort in the firm

Before turning to the determinants of the amount of technical effort in which firms will engage, a few remarks concerning the knowledge produced are in order. Part of it will be in the form of answers to problems arising in the course of the firm's current operations, and thus directly usable. But there will also be an autonomous component involving knowledge not directly related to present production. The two types of knowledge output are joint products for several reasons. Knowledge cannot be channeled along precise lines, so that the results of a particular investigation may lead in unexpected directions. Also, similar technologies can have applications in unrelated markets. In addition, technical effort must be continuous, whereas clearly defined problems in present production arise stochastically. It would be inefficient to limit the use of resources engaged in technical effort to 'troubleshooting'. Nevertheless, there is some positive correlation between the questions asked and the answers provided. Joint production of solutions to problems and of new opportunities takes place partly because the correlation is not perfect, and partly because it is efficient to devote resources to both purposes at once.

In considering the problem of the extent to which firms will engage in technical effort, it must first be remarked that there is no logical necessity for technical effort to be profitable, in the sense of yielding a return to the resources engaged in it in excess of their market value. Nevertheless, the history of the chemical industry in the 19th century and industrial history in the 20th century generally, provide a clear indication that substantial technical effort was often economically justified. In many cases, moreover, the actual amount may seriously have understated the scope for profitable technical effort. For this reason, the following paragraphs focus on possible barriers to full exploitation of the technical opportunities for devoting resources to the production of knowledge.

The firm will engage in technical effort to the extent that expected returns to the resources engaged exceed their cost. This is not an answer but a restatement of the problem. The production of knowledge is peculiar in that the returns are both more uncertain and more indirect than is true for other types of economic activity. We shall return to the problem posed by the absence of a well-defined production function for knowledge (past experience is not a guide in the way that it is for the production of goods). This leaves the fact that the returns from technical effort are in the form of opportunities for changing the mode of production. Their economic value depends on the firm's readiness to respond and on the market effects of such response, as well as on the actual technical benefits that production can derive from the new knowledge. Costs and benefits will thus depend on the extent to which the firm fulfills the behavioral requirements of knowledge-centered operation, on the rhythm of change in its markets, on the nature of its technology, on the structure of the industry, and perhaps on relative factor prices. Each of these requires some elaboration.

In order that technical effort may yield profits the firm must behave in certain ways. These behavioral 'costs' may perhaps best be grasped by considering the case of an entrepreneur who plans to transform technical effort from a part of his own contribution into an organized function of the firm's operations, with formalized procedures and the expenditure of tangible resources. He faces problems with regard to loss of control, an increasing tempo of change, and a continuing drain of resources toward imperfectly predictable ends. As the process of gathering, producing, and using information becomes more extensive and more formal, close control from the top overall phases of the operation becomes impossible. The entrepreneur-turned-manager must rely on the expertise of others and delegate decision-making as well as control. This may prove difficult to do, not least for the energetic entrepreneur used to the efficient simplicity of direct supervision. Secondly, change will be both frequent and substantial in scope for the firm engaging in active technical effort. Not only will there be technical change owing to developments within the firm and to ready response to innovations elsewhere in the industry, but the firm will approximate more closely the model of profit maximization, which implies adjustment to any movement in markets where the firm buys and sells. Technical effort widens the range of adaptability and shortens the reaction time. Management must therefore live with a situation that is unstable in two ways. Not only are new products and processes replacing old ones even while the latter are still viable, but within existing techniques changing conditions lead to changes in practice. The firm must standardize and systematize procedures for change as well as ways of actually carrying out production, a more difficult task to plan and administer. Finally, the firm engaging in substantial technical effort regularly expends resources which clearly do not contribute to present profit, and which may never contribute to profit at all. Research projects may be unsuccessful; costly flexibility in plant scale and factor proportions may not be needed; sophisticated control procedures may produce nothing but reams of data and paperwork. But the firm must accept the necessity of carrying the overhead costs of research and development, planning, engineering, market research, quality control, methods analysis, etc., and of running production operations at more than the minimum static cost achievable.

The return to technical effort will depend on how much change is required to take advantage of the new opportunities, since firms may not exploit knowledge that leads too far afield or may require an abnormally high return to do so. In addition, technical effort will be more profitable when external conditions change frequently and strongly enough to justify continuing expenditure aimed at facilitating adjustment. But the firm does not change only in response to exogenous stimuli, since some of the product of technical effort can be exploited by autonomous change on the part of the firm.

On the technical level, the firm is likely to be knowledge-centered in operation if its technology involves the application of exact scientific knowledge to production. In that case, precise control and rational investigation are necessities, and some technical effort is a part of minimum cost rather than a supplement in the interests of flexibility and future technical progress. Also, the availability of manpower skills, techniques, and information from science lowers the cost of information as an input to technical effort. It is thus no accident that the chemical industry was among the first, if not the first, to have knowledge-centered firms.

A highly competitive situation will stimulate profit maximization, but may make it more difficult for the firm to choose knowledge-centered operation as the solution. The complex matter of industrial structure and its interaction with technical effort is left to the next chapter, with the warning that the approach used here makes it hard to use the traditional static categories of monopoly and competition.

Relatively abundant capital, especially human capital, should lower the cost of a given real investment in technical effort, however that may be measured. However, if the resources used in technical effort are scarce, the knowledge they produce should command a correspondingly high premium, in the sense that there are still easy improvements to be made in the technology. If there are increasing returns to scale in technical effort, it will be held back by a scarcity of the appropriate resources. To the extent that human capital is the bottleneck, rather than capital in general, the extent of technical effort will have an influence on the supply of this factor, which is in large measure specific.

Given the elements that affect the firm's decision as to the amount of technical effort it will undertake, there remains the question of whether the privately determined amount is socially optimal. Three types of arguments suggest that social return may be understated. They involve the problems of appropriability, uncertainty, and returns to scale.

In the absence of monopoly a firm cannot hope to appropriate the full return from technical effort, since knowledge is largely a public good. Part of the knowledge gained becomes available to competitors, and part may fail to yield a return because the firm is not able to make the changes necessary to its application. There are, it is true, certain markets for knowledge, such as the sale or licensing of patents, consulting and design services, but they are far from perfect. However, the static view may overstate the importance of imperfect appropriability. The combination of secrecy, patent protection, and a head start may provide a considerable short-run return, while the technical effort required to imitate the leader may be little lower than his own and depend on the scale of technical effort in the imitating firm. This suggests not only that technical effort can earn a return even from the production of a public good, but also that one element of the return to technical effort is the ease with which knowledge produced outside can be used. Then, too, the knowledge-centered firm may be quite satisfied with short-run appropriability, since it contributes to the obsolescence of its own stock of knowledge by continuing to innovate in the same area. Finally, as I shall argue later, the firm may deliberately engage in technical effort for the benefit of other firms, reaping a return in the form of pecuniary external economies.

There is no question that the production of knowledge is uncertain by comparison with other types of economic production. Perhaps mining offers the best analogy, in terms of unpredictable and substantial shifts in the production function. Uncertainty may reduce the amount of resources firms commit to technical effort, but this is not a necessary outcome. For one thing, the insurance principle suggests that the average return to a number of projects may be more predictable and stable than the return to any one. In addition, technical effort provides a 'balanced portfolio' of returns with its joint products of answers to specific problems (limited return, low uncertainty, direct and immediate economic application) and new production possibilities (uncertain application but high potential return). Finally, risk aversion is not necessarily the dominant pattern of firm behavior. Speculation may take the form of scientific plunges as well as financial ones, and research can be a matter of fashion and status.

Reference has already been made to economies of scale in technical effort. For the case of a research laboratory the division of labor operates as it does in other productive operations, as Beer documents for the Bayer laboratories in the late 19th century[3]). The chances of success for a project will be increased by access to a wide variety of skills, equipment, experience, and information, and there will also be indivisibilities, cases where a massive effort may produce a result not obtainable by longer application of fewer resources. There is also the value of speed itself, especially when technical effort is in response to a change that may be short-lived, and given that appropriability of knowledge is of the dynamic or transitory type. Finally, a part of the cost of undertaking substantial technical effort is the necessary behavioral change in the management of the firm, and this is a fixed cost, independent of the subsequent extent of technical effort.

Scale in technical effort refers not only to absolute amounts, but also to the relationship of technical effort to the size of the firm. If the knowledge-centered firm must operate direct production at higher than minimum cost to get maximum return from technical effort, that effort must be of sufficient scale to yield a return which will cover the increment in production costs[4]). It is this requirement of absolute and relative scale, along with the behavioral constraints for operation in the presence of technical effort, which makes it useful to draw the distinction between knowledge-centered and backward firms, instead of assuming merely some unimodal distribution of firms according to the importance of technical effort in their operation.

Just as technical effort must bear at least a certain relationship to the size of the firm, so, too, this activity may be limited on the upward side by that size. Technical effort is a quasi-fixed cost of production in the short run (given product, technique, and scale), so that the return to the effort depends on the scale of production. This does not mean that there are fixed proportions, with the size of the product market the determining factor in the return to technical effort. A large part of a product's total cost may represent gross return to technical effort, with limited sales, and equilibrium in an area of declining marginal cost[5]).

To sum up, while there are problems in reconciling the private and social optima, there are also reasons which suggest that firms will engage in substantial technical effort, and that this can be profitable despite imperfections on both the demand and the supply side of the market for knowledge. Perhaps the most significant barriers to wider use of technical effort are the necessary initial scale and transitional cost on the one hand, and the absence of fundamental knowledge and appropriate factors of production on the other, especially in certain technical or geographic areas. The first consideration means that timid attempts to invest resources in obtaining more knowledge are likely to do no more than confirm the skepticism of the reluctant manager. The second suggests that public policy can affect technical progress by acting on the supply of trained manpower, by sponsoring fundamental research, and by its policy regarding the market for knowledge.

2. The determinants of technical effort in the chemical industry

> *Il y a trois manières de se ruiner, disait le grand Rothschild: le jeu, les femmes... et les ingénieurs. Les deux premières sont plus agréables... mais la dernière est plus sûre. [There are three roads to ruin, Rothschild used to say: gambling, women... and engineers. The first two are more pleasant... but the last is the surest.]*
>
> Detoeuf

The preceding discussion of technical effort and of the external factors affecting its role in the firm has brought out the relevance of education, of public policy, and of the entrepreneur. We shall now examine the impact of these factors on the chemical industry in France, Germany, and Switzerland.

2.1. Education

Perhaps the most frequently stressed factor in Germany's lead over France in the chemical industry was her supply of trained chemists, and the excellence and scope of the facilities for training them. Chemical education may not have been considered by all as the universal panacea that Liebig held it to be, but its role in bringing the German chemical industry to its position of leadership was commonly acknowledged, while the shortcomings of French training were viewed as a major source of retardation [6]). Switzerland had close educational ties to Germany, and Basle had a tradition of interest in science and education, although the connection between the University and the industry in that city was tenuous in the 19th century[7]). Nor is it possible to ascribe any major role in promoting the industry to the ETH (Polytechnic Institute) founded in Zurich in 1855.

Up to the middle of the century France led the way not only in chemistry, but also in the applications of laboratory findings to industry. Men such as Gay-Lussac, Frémy, and Thénard collaborated with St. Gobain, while the twenty-one-year-old Kuhlmann taught chemistry at the University of Lille before becoming a manufacturer[8]). The men who organized and directed early chemical education in Germany, from Liebig to Kekule, studied in Paris, because they preferred the practical, laboratory-centered approach to the sterile idealism of German universities at that time[9]). Why this situation changed remains for the historians of science or of ideas to answer, but there is no doubt that it did. By the end of the century an almost complete divorce had occurred between science, especially academic science, and industry. French chemistry, and the universities in general, were marked by rigidity, overcentralization and official theories, and a total lack of interest in application[10]). Professors did not devote time to laboratory instruction, the keystone of Liebig's system, whereas students were too preoccupied with competitive examinations to have the time to develop techniques and undertake research projects of their own[11]). The great English chemists of the middle years of the century also lacked interest either in applying their science to the practical arts or in training young chemists[12]).

The strength of French education in science was limited to mathematics, physics, and mechanics, the province of the *Grandes Ecoles*, which took the best students. The economic picture was even more discouraging. Professors were underpaid, laboratories inadequate and poorly supported. This was particularly serious in organic chemistry, where scale and organization are necessary in laboratories and libraries to keep abreast of what was even then a large body of knowledge. Furthermore, studies took time, and chemistry, which was a low-prestige field of study, attracted few people who could afford to study long enough[13]).

In this maze of criticisms, of a kind frequently heard in France in more recent times as well, it is necessary to try to isolate those that had a marked effect on the progress of the chemical industry. We shall put aside for now the important question of the responsibility of business in the state of technical education. But the opposite causal mechanism was significant as well. Centralization hurt considerably, especially when coupled with rigid programs and official theories. Thus, when Kekule worked out the structure of the benzene molecule in 1865, opening the way to orderly progress in the maze of new organic compounds, the theory was accepted by some French chemists but not by all. Since Wurtz, who defended the use of Kekule's structural formula, was in Nancy, whereas Berthelot, who attacked it, was in Paris, the official theory remained the old one[14]). Such sterile quarrels wer no substitute for the systematic experimental work of the German labs. It is worth noting that Liebig was at times quite wrong and dogmatic, but a lesser degree of centralization and Liebig's own emphasis on the laboratory prevented this from having a stultifying effect on research. The second major loss was due to the gap between the university, where applications and technology had no place, and the low-grade practical schools, insufficient as these may have been. Until 1872 there were no schools of industrial chemistry, and those founded after that time did not compare in prestige with the *Grandes Ecoles*, which for their part gave no emphasis at all to chemical subjects[15]).

This picture seems very negative, perhaps because those who have described it were examining the educational system as an *ex post* cause of the failure of the industry to develop rapidly, especially as compared to that of the 'Prussians'. In later years, when new industries based on physical chemistry became significant, France was in a better position. Her engineers had excellent training in mechanics and electricity, as well as thermodynamics. They were also competent plant managers, once there was sufficient scale to warrant the presence of an engineer in addition to the chemical men[16]).

French writers gave the impression, when analyzing the corresponding state of affairs in Germany, that the government, the universities, and industry worked smoothly together for their mutual good, and that a German chemist was indeed a privileged person. This was undoubtedly more nearly the case than in either France or Britain, but German sources paint a less idyllic picture. More important, the pattern of education in the universities and *Technische Hochschulen* does not explain some of the most striking features of the industry. On the first point, there were occasional complaints about the status of chemists, the attitude of the government, and comments that industry profited little from academic research[17]). More seriously, the course of training was long and arduous, and salaries were not high for young chemists. But the role played by chemists in the development of the great firms in the industry cannot be predicted from the methodical, scholarly, pure chemical training given in the universities. And with respect to the exceptional qualities of organizational, executive, and entrepreneurial talents shown by a number of men in the industry, one cannot say that the engineers did better than the chemists.

The supply of technical manpower to German industry was, however, well assured by the universities, the *Hochschulen*, and a number of lower schools. Since in France the influence of manufacturers on education was never more than indirect, this would seem to be a clear case of inadequate factor supply. Moreover, this factor would seem to have been especially specific, in the sense that it was responsible for just those features of growth, namely rapid and autonomous technical change, which this study has adopted as criteria of good performance. But the economist who examines the role of factor supply must also look at marginal product and price, which will tend to equality unless the market is restricted. And the relative prices or salaries of technical men would lead to the conclusion that they were scarce and more productive, at the margin, in Germany[18]). Either the French entrepreneurs did not pay chemists their marginal product, or they used them so as to make that marginal product lower than it was in Germany, despite the contrary prediction theory would suggest, given the relative factor scarcities. In either case, the answer must be sought in entrepreneurial behavior. It is possible, of course, that French chemists were poor, and therefore worth less to the firm just because of their weaker training. Yet there was no rush to hire foreign chemists, or to send young Frenchmen abroad. Even this might be in keeping with the political temper of the time, but the same held true in England. Finally, it is not clear that French chemists received poor training, since a considerable amount of scientific research continued to flow from France.

There is no question that the pure research done by academic men had a major influence on the development of the industry. The names of Hoffmann, Kekule, Heumann, Baeyer, and Le Chatelier stand out among many. But this work was available to all, except as 'official' theories or neglect of the literature prevented its diffusion, as was in part the case in France.

On balance, it is probably true that French technical education supplied an inadequate number of graduates and trainees, and did not train those few effectively for industrial research and operations. But this inadequacy is with respect to the size of France's chemical industry and the opportunities for it, not with respect to the demand for technical manpower actually obtaining. In terms of job opportunities, and of the duties chemists were called on to perform in industry, not to mention promotion to leading positions, the chemists were too many and often overtrained. Indeed, the complaints from industry that chemists lacked the training and attitude for industrial research came only with the World War, when the industry was propelled into great technical and economic activity by the war emergency[19]). Education was a real factor, but it does not hold the key to the disparity in the amount of technical effort in chemicals on the two sides of the Rhine.

2.2. Government

Before considering the importance of entrepreneurial factors, it is necessary to consider the role of public policy on the development of the chemical industry. This involves chiefly commercial policy, regulation of industrial activity on nuisance or other grounds, and patent law.

The role of patents and of particular provisions of patent law in furthering technical progress and industrial growth is a complex subject, and one that cannot be fully treated here. Many writers ascribe significance to patent laws in the history of chemical production in Europe, largely because of the fuchsine case, or because the German industry's strength was reflected in a powerful and carefully nurtured patent position. The facts may be reviewed briefly[20]). In France, the law of 1844 regulated the protection of inventors, and attempts to change it were not successful until well after World War I. Under this law, patents were granted without prior examination by the government[21]). More important, it provided for patent protection for a new *product*, even if another process was found whereby this product could be made. At least the law was so interpreted. In Germany, a unified patent law did not exist until 1877, so that German firms were able to use foreign technology at will, and the law reflected the needs of an already vigorous knowledge-centered industry.

An important factor in shaping the character of the all-German patent law was the experience of the chemical industry with alizarin after 1869. The pioneering work of Caro, of the BASF, in developing the Graebe–

Lieberman synthesis into a practical process was not protected, and imitators forced the price down rapidly[22]). The leading chemical firms wanted a law which improved the market for knowledge, i.e., which made the returns to technical effort somewhat more appropriable. But the law only protected the knowledge-centered firm which was prepared to devote substantial resources to working out new technology and then to exploit its intellectual property aggressively. It did little for the isolated inventor or for the firm that tried to earn a pure rent on some technical advantage it enjoyed. The German law specified both a patent search, to ensure novelty and substance in patents, and the limitation of protection to processes, as opposed to products. It also specified substantial and increasing fees, to ensure that a patent holder did not block others while failing to work the patented process himself. Finally, added protection was provided the patent holder by *Zusatzpatente* after 1891, covering applications and improvements.

Switzerland did without a patent law even longer than Germany. The Swiss specialized in complex products with limited markets, and felt that the large German firms would not take rapid advantage of their lack of formal protection. On the other hand, the Swiss could use German patents without permission or cost so long as there was no Swiss patent law. They finally introduced a law when German pressure to do so became insistent.

The French law was intended to encourage individual inventors, and was more suitable for mechanical than for chemical inventions. It is tempting to ascribe the lack of progress in organic chemicals to the product versus process feature, and this was indeed important in the fuchsine case, but there was no inherent reason for the law to remain in force throughout the period, when it was clearly realized that it was not suitable for process industries[23]). But attempts to change the law were resisted and defeated. One reason given was that a process patent would allow large firms to force out the small inventor by changing in a minor way the manufacture of a product[24]). This reasoning was considered typical of the French *bas de laine* mentality, which was unwilling to see industrial progress where this meant concentration, reallocation, or occupational mobility. An important additional reason for the failure to emulate the more modern German or even British scheme may well have been that the government would have to set up a substantial technical establishment to implement the changes. Finally, it must be said that French manufacturers had a deep-seated distrust of patents to the extent that these involved disclosure. They much preferred secrecy as protection against imitators. It is difficult to say whether this might have been changed by a German type of law, strict in the matter of granting patents, but a strong defender of the patent holder once his right to protection was recognized.

In the matter of commercial policy, French chemical manufacturers were no exception to the frequent call for protection typical of industrialists[25]). The impression one receives is that it was almost impossible, in French business circles, to be other than protectionist in public utterances, much as American businessmen of the mid-20th century cannot stray from advocating fiscal orthodoxy. Protectionism had few rivals, especially after 1870 when the free-trading Imperial regime disappeared[26]). The protectionist case was complicated by the fact that chemicals were an input into industries that were important, or that claimed to need protection not because they were inefficient but to compensate for more costly inputs[27]).

French manufacturers claimed protection on the grounds of a permanent disadvantage with respect to foreign competition, rather than invoking the infant industry argument. The usual reasons given related to the cost of coal, due partly to poor deposits, but increased further by a tariff intended to protect marginal producers in older areas particularly, and high taxes caused by France's military and colonial expenditures[28]). The usual practice was to ask for more protection or at least the same level, with any and all arguments used to justify the position taken, the implication being that protection was the normal state and free or freer trade an unorthodox departure. Manufacturers also used strategic arguments and fancied cost disadvantages in labor and capital, with respect to Germany or England[29]).

The activity of the French government, with respect to regulation of business, was a frequent source of complaints. In general, regulations were ubiquitous but slow to change when change involved either fiscal loss, technical problems, or conflicting interests. Thus, there were heavy taxes on alcohol and salt, which did not take into account that these were important raw materials as well as consumption goods with conveniently low price elasticities of demand. As an example, the early ammonia–soda process of Schloessing and Rolland, which antedated Solvay's success, required the use of brine produced underground by pumping water into salt deposits. This was prohibited by the authorities on the basis of a law forbidding extraction of salt except under direct government control[30]).

Long after the introduction of the mantle for burning gas, French law still required lighting gas to contain benzol, which had originally provided luminescence but was now a nuisance. Similarly, the legislation requiring a licensed pharmacist to be in direct control of any manufacture of pharmaceutical products continued in force long after this industry had become 'chemical' and production required technical rather than scientific supervision. On the other hand, the government hesitated to interfere with trade in fertilizers, on the grounds of laissez faire, even though hearings brought out that widespread fraud and lack of standards and official testing were in large part responsible for the reluctance of French farmers to use the new materials[31]).

Businessmen also felt that industry would benefit from more rapid concentration, but that the law against combinations, dating back to Napoleon, prevented this. How real this constraint was remains doubtful. Finally, there were recurrent difficulties, in France as elsewhere, with nuisances associated with chemical manufacture. However, in this instance the authorities usually helped, since factories were forced to move out of urban areas where there was insufficient room to expand, or were forced to make better use of by-products[32]).

Less is known about the role of government regulation and commercial policy in Germany and Switzerland, perhaps because there was less need to assign blame for failures. The chemical industry seldom sought protection, an exception being German soda manufacturers, since it was largely export-oriented. As for regulation of industry, these governments seem to have been more responsive to the needs of new industries, and reasonable in fiscal matters and the like. More important, the government was willing to undertake activities that benefited the industry, such as agricultural research, fertilizer-testing stations, and the provision of adequate consular services in customer countries.

It is in this respect, one may say, that the French government most strongly hindered the progress of the industry. It seems to have been unable to take initiatives that required technical effort. The exceptions were areas in which a tradition of state action had been established under Napoleon, or in which the state expected to derive substantial fiscal advantages, such as a monopoly. This unwillingness of the government to supply a technical infrastructure was noted in Great Britain as well, but there at least the dedication to laissez faire was reasonably consistent. The French administration was still quite mercantilistic in many respects, and in addition the unresolved social tensions in 19th-century France made the government the guardian of an uneasy balance, which it maintained by favoring established interests. This combination of distaste for new technical involvement, coupled with a bias against change in an atmosphere of persistent interference in the economic sphere, was detrimental to industrialization in general, but it affected the chemical industry strongly. Knowledge-centered operation would have benefited from complementary technical initiatives on the part of government. But at the least it required some institutional adaptation. Where change was hindered by the delicate social balance and low mobility, technical effort on the part of government could, but in France did not, find ways of minimizing the unfavorable impact of generally constructive change.

The situation was not improved by the fact that entrepreneurs tended to react by more demands for state aid, thus intensifying the pressures responsible for many of the negative effects of public policy. Perhaps the problem was that France, and therefore the French state, was not so clearly committed to industrialization as were her eastern neighbors, and cared more for managing social change than for providing a favorable terrain for industry. Finally, it must be said that Germany and Switzerland had perhaps fewer established interests with which the new industry came into conflict. Germany industrialized later than France, and did not have a commitment to natural dyestuffs and the complex dyeing technology associated with them; nor, as we have noted, had it built up a large Leblanc soda industry. The Swiss industry conflicted little with any local interests, except for sanitary problems in the early days of the Basle industry. But this qualification does not, in my opinion, greatly weaken the above point, namely that the state significantly hindered the growth of the chemical industry in France, whereas it had a permissive or encouraging role in the other two countries.

2.3. Entrepreneurship

One factor remains to be considered in analyzing the performance of the three countries in chemical production, and the preceding discussion suggests that it must share, with transport and government, the brunt of the responsibility for explaining the behavior of the industry. There is a sizeable literature on the role of entrepreneurship in industrialization, and considerable attention has been paid to the French case in particular[33]). It is not appropriate to review this work here, and the following comments apply only to the behavior of firms in the chemical sector. Emphasis will be placed on the attitude of entrepreneurs in the three countries toward technical effort and technical change, and toward expansion and diversification under the stimulus of changing technology.

The typical German chemical firm began under the direction of businessmen, seconded by technically trained employees or associates[34]). The most striking characteristic of these firms was the willingness of entrepreneurs to entrust the operation of the firm to technical men and gradually to shift the focus of decision-making away from the factory and toward the laboratory. A striking example of such a transformation is provided by Bayer. The firm was founded in 1863 by a merchant who traded in natural dyestuffs, and first manufactured fuchsine. Growth was slow for the first two decades, during which time technical supervision was largely in the hands of foremen or *Meister*, with no formal training[35]). Even when chemists were hired, first with vocational and later with academic training, their tasks involved the supervision and improvement of manufacturing processes. True research was not begun until around 1880, when three young chemists were hired and sent to work in university laboratories, considered more conducive to scientific work than the plant[36]). Beer notes the halting and difficult course of the early research effort, but it is perhaps more noteworthy that the attempt was made at all, and in the midst of a severe crisis in alizarin prices at that. It is true that the most useful result for Bayer of the first step in the direction of knowledge-centered operation was to acquire the services of Carl Duisberg. Fifteen years later this productive chemist was in effective charge of the firm, and organizing its move to Leverkusen on the Rhine.

It has often been noted that German chemical firms made considerable use of technical and scientific personnel in a managerial capacity. Duisberg is an outstanding example, but by no means unique[37]). He was not only a good executive, but also the driving force behind the series of agreements and consolidations that culminated in the formation of the IG-Farben trust in 1925. He first suggested a union between the German dyestuff manufacturers in a memorandum written after a trip to the United States in 1904[38]). The significant point, however, is that nontechnical entrepreneurs were willing to hire and promote these men, to back them in their decision to invest in technical effort, and to allow the operations of the firm to grow and change in response to the new technology being developed[39]).

There were important consequences of this attitude. One was the magnitude of the research effort, and frequent expansion and diversification dictated by the results of this effort. Here, too, capital followed where science led, and funds were not begrudged even where profits seemed distant and uncertain. The classical example is that of the BASF, which invested at least 18 million marks in the development of synthetic indigo, and did not sell a pound of it until 18 years after research was begun[40]). Production had to be on a corresponding scale, so that export markets were a necessity. Further impetus to large scale was provided by the need to integrate in all directions, in order to obtain the right raw materials or intermediaries, to exploit by-products, or to innovate in the use of new products[41]). Other aspects of the business also were affected by the domination of the chemists and engineers, who introduced exact control of manufacture and cost accounting, and brought science to bear on the selling function in the form of application research and technical service.

In Switzerland as well, nontechnical entrepreneurs began most of the firms, and scientific research soon came to be the main source of growth and profits. But the leading Basle firms developed very differently from their German counterparts[42]). The entrepreneurs behaved in a much more traditional way, and control of the business remained for a long time in a few hands, if not within a family. Financial management was prudent, expansion gradual, and discretion, not to say secrecy, as much the rule as in France[43]). Only in one respect did the entrepreneurs depart from the traditional model familiar to analysts of French or British economic retardation, but this proved crucial. They were willing to spend money on technical effort without any assurance of return, and to modify their production as the results required it. In particular, the Swiss readily abandoned any line in which the technological difficulties were no longer great enough to make chemical sophistication the cost-determining factor. In this reliance on progress as the key to safety, they resembled the Germans. In other respects, including the appearance of their plants and the lack of sophistication of their production equipment, they were much like the French[44]).

Before discussing the many shortcomings attributed to French entrepreneurs, it is well to realize that some of them were able innovators, and many were competent managers and good businessmen. Such firms as Kuhlmann, Péchiney, Coignet, and St. Gobain prospered throughout the 19th century, and all continued into the 20th, emerging after World War II as modern firms able to compete in the world market and responsible for a fair share of research and innovation. Even before 1914, especially in the period after 1890–96, a number of new firms and industries developed in France, in chemicals as well as other fields. Electrochemicals, light metals, liquefied gases, and artificial textiles are cases in point. But it is well to note that, while existing chemical companies were important in these areas in Germany, they played a surprisingly small part in launching new developments in France[45]. Finally, in discussing chemical manufacturers, the one firm representing France in the production of dyestuffs, the Société des Matières Colorantes de St. Denis, should not be forgotten. Faced with the same disadvantages and foreign competition that seem to furnish ample excuse for the industry as a whole, this firm though it remained small, continued to produce at a profit and had its share of innovations[46]. Young Eduard Sandoz, later the founder of a Basle firm, began his career in the chemical industry as a commercial employee of the firm (1878)[47].

Despite these exceptions, it would seem that the record of French entrepreneurs suffers by comparison with their opposite numbers to the east. There are three aspects, in particular, of their role which are worth mention. These are:

1. The entrepreneur as an organizer of factors of production.
2. The attitude towards science and technical change.
3. Change and risk as menaces.

1. French entrepreneurs were to an extent the victims of their own competence. The manufacturers were often able technical men, used to directing all aspects of the business, from labor relations to starting up new processes. They either owned the business or were the *gérant* in a *Société en Commandité*, with sole responsibility for policy and management[48]. St. Gobain, the oldest French company, was a *Société Anonyme* as early as 1830, but there, too, a small group had complete control over all phases of the operation. From the start, therefore, the entrepreneur

was in a sense the company, rather than merely its chief executive. The factors of production, from engineers to raw materials, were auxiliaries to be used as he saw fit, rather than components whose cooperation it was his responsibility to promote. He was a workman with tools and not a conductor facing an orchestra. As long as his competence sufficed, say in the first generation, this method was acceptable. But when expansion or diversification were necessary, or a new process had to be developed or adapted, he was unwilling to surrender the necessary measure of control[49]). Thus he distrusted banks, and stockholders unless they remained sleeping partners. He resisted the advent of the engineer or chemist who knew more science than he himself, and railed against a government that did not insulate him from changes in demand, competition, or the economic environment. The one phase of business most clearly his to retain, namely sales, he often left to middle men who were poor transmitters of new requirements or better products[50]). By contrast, the BASF in 1889 integrated sales which had been handled by a Stuttgart firm, with the parent company due to the growing importance of technical service. Entrepreneurs often displayed great activity in making improvements in their plant without changing the fundaments of their technology, but such steps were in the long run no match for sweeping changes exemplified by the Solvay process in the soda industry.

2. To the French chemical entrepreneur, business was based on a favorable resource position and a stable market not too exposed to the cold wind of competition. He engaged in continued effort to cut costs, to improve yields, and to eliminate waste due to unsalable products. Such technical advantages as he enjoyed, owing to his ingenuity and to long experience, were protected by secrecy much more frequently than by patents. As we noted, the latter involved at least partial disclosure, and could lead to costly and uncertain litigation. But change of a more drastic sort, or scientific inquiry into the nature of the processes applied by the firm, were of no interest. The stock of knowledge was a static sort of asset, rather than a dynamic base for further exploration. This was perhaps the greatest difference between the French and German industrialists. It is only necessary to compare the statement of the St. Gobain management that the 'true wealth' of the company was its pyrites mine, with that of Heinrich von Brunck, who stated that the German firms had such a great lead, because of their stock of knowledge and continuing research invest-

ment, that even training of foreign chemists in Germany would not allow other countries to overcome it[51]).

In Germany, the chemist was looked on as an adjunct to a continuing technical effort, needing training. His work might be only distantly connected with any of the company's present products, but it fitted in with other work in the company, and with the growing body of knowledge contained in the literature, to advance the solution of technical problems, and thus to provide new products, processes, or methods. Obsolescence, competition, and disclosure eroded the profitability of the stock of knowledge, so that a part of the effort was of a maintenance nature. But a substantial part was net investment. In France, on the other hand, chemical work was apt to be a one-shot effort, brought on by a threat from outside. The chemist was either used as a laboratory assistant, in routine jobs, or expected to solve complex problems at once, at slight expense[52]). The entrepreneur, who often was not even able to ask the right questions of his technical people, was thus confirmed in his skepticism regarding science and scientists.

As has already been noted, French innovation was not unknown, far from it, but it rarely was led by existing firms. Thus, the assets of experience, capital, and the like were in the hands of the old firms, while innovations were seeking resources in a capital market that distrusted science more than did the manufacturers. By contrast, the German and Swiss firms were led to innovate by the often unforeseen results of research, and in any case were well placed to take advantage of new knowledge developed elsewhere, for example at universities.

3. Resistance to change in France was not limited to a negative attitude toward scientific research. A great concern for conserving and consolidating *positions acquises* dominated much of entrepreneurial attitudes. This was evident in such research as was done by firms. St. Gobain's attitude was perhaps typical. All research was justified as continued watchfulness over developments abroad that might threaten the company's position[53]). Similarly, Péchiney and St. Gobain both bought English equipment and licenses to help their Leblanc plants meet the threat from the Solvay process, and they adapted and improved some of the modifications as in the Weldon–Péchiney process. But the only substantial work done in France on the ammonia–soda process was done by Schloessing and Rolland, and not by any of the leading firms. Firms were reluctant to

diversify, since this meant entering a new sector or industry, and also to expand unless it was to protect a leading position[54]).

In order to defend against change, once it was assumed that the firm could not adapt or innovate so as to benefit from it, liquidity and economy were necessary. This meant freedom from banks, a minimum of fixed assets and fast depreciation, and, finally, low overhead, including 'unproductive' research and pilot plant facilities[55]). Given protection from foreign competition, and an absence of aggressive elements at home, the process of change could be postponed for a long time. Finally, the new ways were adopted when they became well known and, by the same token, less profitable.

Although cautious and conservative management was the norm for French firms, speculation was by no means absent from the business scene. In finance especially, there was a tradition of *affaires*, deals or propositions of dubious soundness but dramatic possibilities. What was notably lacking, on the other hand, was the willingness among established firms in industry and finance to take moderate risks over long periods. Yet this is precisely what knowledge-centered operation implies. As an example, consider again the case of La Fuchsine. As previously discussed, it seems clear that the object of the founders was not to enter the chemical industry via the new field of synthetic dyestuffs. As dyers, they wished to exploit a temporary monopoly of considerable short-run profitability. A new dyestuff had caught the public fancy after being introduced at the Imperial court, and, because it happened to be a synthetic material rather than a natural one, a patent monopoly was possible. Speed and legal strength were thus more essential than technical capital. Looking at the matter in this way, it becomes easier to understand several atypical features of the case. One is the direct participation of a bank in a new industrial enterprise. Another is the amount of capital, 4 million francs, and the speed with which the company was begun. Finally, it is clear that Renard and his technical and manufacturing associates were willing to allow control to rest in the hands of the financial interests, again rather atypical behavior for French businessmen[56]). Other evidence as well is consistent with the view that Lyons considered the new chemical discoveries the basis for short-term *affaires* rather than long-term *enterprises*. When a representative of the young *Farbwerke* at Höchst came to Lyons to sell his new aldehyde green, Renard was interested, but on condition that he be given a monopoly on sales of the dye in France for one year[57]). And when smuggling of dyes from Germany and Switzerland, as well as the prospect of rapid obsolescence for fuchsine dimmed the prospects of the company, the only reasonable course was liquidation. Since no continuing technical effort was contemplated, it was impossible to consider early difficulties as the cost of building up the firm's stock of knowledge, to use the language of this study.

The case of La Fuchsine should not be overstressed. The failure of one early venture is not noteworthy in itself, and we have neglected dozens of unsuccessful ventures in all the countries. As far as the chemical industry is concerned, the real loss was not due to the failure of the company, but to its temporary success in enforcing a monopoly and discouraging other technical work in France. And yet one wonders. By 1870 the company was liquidated, and there was nothing to stop new ventures in synthetic dyestuffs. Technology had made rapid strides, so that the old aniline dyes no longer dominated the market. Yet there was no rebirth of activity in France. It is true that competitors had acquired an impressive head start, but not, surely, a prohibitive lead. The German and Swiss firms were small at this early stage. They, too, were participating in the teething troubles of the new industry, but temporary profits were used to build up technical expertise, and temporary difficulties treated as start-up costs, in effect.

David Landes has called the attitude of German entrepreneurs a commitment to technical efficiency, largely independent of any economic calculus concerning the relative merits of change and the status quo[58]). This is similar to what might be called the 'propensity to engage in technical effort', except that I would focus on the decision to invest resources in the production of knowledge rather than on the adoption of the newest and most capital-intensive methods of production (of goods). To be sure, a bias in favor of rapid replacement of techniques and equipment made for greater returns to technical effort, along the lines discussed earlier in this chapter. As an example of the German commitment to rapid obsolescence, chemists in Duisberg's laboratory at Bayer were enjoined by contract from accepting employment with a competitor for two years after separation from the company. After that time, it was felt, their knowledge of proprietary information would have little commercial value[59]).

3. Conclusion

Knowledge-centered operation is a gamble on the technical possibilities and their economic relevance, i.e., on the return to technical effort. Because it turns out, *ex post*, that the gamble was a good one for the chemical industry in 19th-century Europe, identifying the sources of the industry's growth reduces largely to finding the factors affecting the decisions to take the gamble. Market conditions have little to contribute, since a difficult position may be just as conducive to a drastic shift in approach as success in the traditional way of organizing production. The supply of human capital is more relevant, except that it, too, is in part endogenous. Chemical education prospered where chemists were in demand. Public policy contributed a more favorable environment in Germany, in the sense of supporting some basic technical effort for producing highly 'public' knowledge, and in responding to the institutional needs of knowledge-centered firms. There remains entrepreneurship as the leading explanatory factor, if only as a residual. While we have not been able to explain why entrepreneurs in France were unwilling to engage heavily in technical effort, we have identified the particular traits that made them behave in this way. Technical effort implied rapid change, loss of control by the individual entrepreneur, and commitment of resources to uncertain, and in any case postponed, profitable ends. As the Swiss case shows, by heavy commitment to technical effort and to the change it implied, firms could avoid the gigantism and financial openness characteristic of the great German *Konzern*, and which French entrepreneurs so wished to avoid. Family control, free from supervision by banks and stockholders, was not excluded by knowledge-centered operation, but technical and product stability and high liquidity were.

Given the distaste of established firms for technical effort, the French industry was hurt by unfavorable conditions in capital markets and in the environment provided by government. Banks wanted no part of long-term industrial participation, especially not in untried ventures, while public policy shied away from technical initiatives that might have allowed it to overcome the constraints imposed by a precarious social balance. Potential innovators had little influence and so could neither raise funds nor exploit their knowledge by selling it. When the emergency of 1914 jarred French industry loose, progress in chemicals was rapid. Knowledge was pooled, restrictions in capital markets, patent policy, regulation of transport, and such disappeared, and maximum output rather than stable profits and high liquidity became the goals. The sharp change in performance is in part illusory, in that production without regard to cost is always easier than in a competitive market, while much of the knowledge needed was standard and freely known by that time. Yet it does show that France's lag was not due to lack of resources, or to any inherent weakness in managerial or technical endowment.

Notes

1. G. Stigler, Production and Distribution in the Short Run, in: *Readings in the Theory of Income Distribution* (1950), pp. 119–142, especially the graph on p. 131.
2. C. P. Kindleberger, after Svennilson, has referred to the capacity of an economy to transform. Translated to the level of the firm, this is a useful concept to describe the effects of technical effort, with the proviso that there is no longer a fixed technological constraint in the present case. *Economic Development*, 2nd ed. (1965), ch. 10.
3. J. Beer, *The Emergence of the German Dye Industry* (1959), p. 71.
4. Assume that a knowledge-centered firm must increase costs of production by 1%, and that direct outlays on technical effort yield 10% net. Then technical effort must be 10% at least of manufacturing cost in order to break even.
5. The organic specialty firms of Basle provide an example of this type of operation, which obviously precludes perfect competition.
6. On education in Germany, see: L. F. Haber, ch. 5; C. Duisberg, *Meine Lebenserinnerungen* (1933); H. Flechtner, *Carl Duisberg* (1959); F. Redlich, *Die volkswirtschaftliche Bedeutung der deutschen Teerfarbenindustrie* (1914). The most extensive treatments of French chemical education are E. Grandmougin, *L'enseignement de la chimie industrielle en France* (1917); E. Fleurent, *Les industries chimiques en France et en Allemagne*, I and II (1915–16); A. Haller, *Les industries chimiques et pharmaceutiques. Exposition de Paris 1900* (1903).
7. A. Bürgin, pp. 90, 93.
8. St. Gobain, *Produits chimiques* (1949); M. Dumas, Le progrès dans l'industrie chimique, *Cahiers de l'ISEA*, no. 123 (March 1962), p. 18. Kuhlmann himself was Alsatian.
9. O. Witt, Die Entwicklung der deutschen chemischen Industrie im 19.Jahrhundert, *Die chemische Industrie*, 7 (1903), p. 12.
10. E. Fleurent, I, 80–81; A. Haller, I, lxxvii.
11. E. Grandmougin (1917), p. 20; Baud, *Les industries chimiques régionales de la France* (1922), p. 39.

Full bibliographical data are given in the Bibliography at the end of the book.

12. J. Beer, p. 15.
13. E. Grandmougin (1917), p. 59.
14. E. Fleurent, I, p. 39.
15. The first schools teaching industrial chemistry were in Lille (1872), Lyons (1883), and Paris (1883). The Lyons school, the first to be associated with the university, was at first judged 'dangerously practical' by the university inspector. *Lyon et la région lyonnaise en 1906* (1906), II, p. 355. See also F. George, *La rénovation de l'industrie chimique française* (1917), pp. 429–430.
16. M. Fauque, *L'évolution économique de la grande industrie chimique en France* (1932), pp. 157–160.
17. B. Rassow, *Die chemische Industrie* (1925), pp. 9, 89; C. Duisberg, p. 65.
18. L. F. Haber, pp. 188–190, gives fragmentary salary data for Germany, Britain, and France. These are not comparable, but it seems clear (as he says) that the Britisher was paid far less than the German, and the French chemist less than that. Prestige, possibilities of advancement, purchasing power, and the general level of wages in the country all accentuated the British lag, and did not, on balance, reduce the even greater one in France.
19. H. Hauser, Rapport general, in: *Association Nationale d'Expansion Economique*, Enquête..., p. 22.
20. L. F. Haber, pp. 200–204; E. and P. Grandmougin, *La réorganisation de l'industrie chimique en France* (1918), pp. 209 ff; E. Fleurent, II, pp. 120 ff. The role of patents in inorganic chemicals was less important, except in such cases as the Solvay process. The basic process was often in the public domain, and engineering improvements were usually kept secret.
21. Hence the familiar notation: "breveté SGDG" (Sans Garantie Du Gouvernement).
22. K. Oberdorffer, p. 68.
23. One author claims that the failure of France to develop the dyestuffs industry was due less to the patent law than to offical hindrances aimed at protecting the madder growers of Provence, who were finally ruined by synthetic alizarin after 1870. See R. Baumgartner, *Die wirtschaftliche Bedeutung der chemischen Industrie in Basel* (1947), p. 24. This problem of government and regulation versus technical change is treated below, but it is interesting to note that the trousers of the French army were colored red in order to provide a market for domestic madder, and that this custom continued until 1914, even though German alizarin had long before replaced the natural product. G. Keppeler, Chemisches auf der Weltausstellung zu Paris im Jahre 1900, in: *Sammlung chemischer und chemischtechnischer Vorträge* (1901), VI, p. 33.
24. E. and P. Grandmougin, *Réorganisation* (1918), p. 211. This type of patent law also favored a large number of inventions, rather than the most efficient and equitable promotion of a few major ones. See E. Fleurent, II, p. 120.
25. See, among others, *Enquête parlementaire sur le régime économique* (1870); M. Suilliot, *Réponses au questionnaire du Conseil Supérieur du Commerce et de l'Industrie* (1890); Syndicat Général des Produits Chimiques, *L'industrie chimique et les droits de douanes* (1918).

26. Free traders made their points almost apologetically, and were careful not to deny the arguments of protectionist entrepreneurs, but only to claim that in a particular case tariffs hurt and did not help. Thus in the 1918 study of the Syndicat Général, one firm, the 'Matières Colorantes de St. Denis' (the only surviving French maker of synthetic dyestuffs before the War) asked for low duties on basic chemicals which were an important input. Its note, unsigned, was printed in the report, but it was rejected by the Syndicat and not mentioned in the table of contents. *Syndicat Général des Produits Chimiques* (1918), pp. 168–180.

27. M. Suilliot, pp. 4–5; Syndicat Commercial et Industriel de Lyon, *Travaux de la Chambre Syndicale, 1873–1893* (1894), pp. 37–38.

28. *Enquête parlementaire*, (1870), p. 79; V. K. Löffl, pp. 58–59.

29. *Syndicat Général, passim*.

30. M. Fauque, *L'évolution économique de la grande industrie chimique en France*, p. 43. The commemorative book of the company which finally worked the process suggests that this may not have been the final cause for abandoning the venture in 1858, though the matter remains unclear. See: *Les Soudières Réunies, 1855–1955* (1955). The tax problems are also discussed by E. Fleurent, II, pp. 110 ff.

31. Ministère de l'Agriculture, du Commerce et des Travaux Publics, *Enquête sur les engrais industriels* (1865), *passim*. The law of 1867, passed after these hearings, remained a dead letter, and nothing was done until 1888. L. Bargeron, *Le Commerce des Engrais* (1906), p. 78.

32. M. Laferrère, *Lyon, ville industrielle* (1960), pp. 29–33; see also R. Maunier, *La distribution géographique des industries* (1908).

33. For a recent discussion, see C. P. Kindleberger's essay, The Post-war Resurgence of the French Economy, in: *In Search of France* (1963), pp. 118 ff. A less scholarly, but entertaining, treatment is A. Detoeuf, *Propos de O. L. Barenton, Confiseur* (1958).

34. See E. Fischer, Meister, Lucius und Brüning, die Gründer der Farbwerke Hoechst, AG, *Tradition*, III, no. 2 (May 1958); Pinnow, *Werksgeschichte der Farbenfabriken, vorm. F. Bayer & Co.* (1938); C. Schuster, *Badische Anilin- und Soda-Fabrik, AG: Ein Beitrag zur Geschichte der chemischen Technik* (n.d.).

35. J. Beer, pp. 74–80.

36. H. J. Flechtner, *Carl Duisberg: vom Chemiker zum Wirtschaftsführer* (1959), pp. 64–66.

37. Others were Brunck and Bosch of the BASF, and Witt of Cassella.

38. The document bore the title 'Denkschrift über die Vereinigung der deutschen Farbenfabriken'. It is reprinted in his *Abhandlungen, Vorträge und Reden aus den Jahren 1882–1921* (1923).

39. See A. Detoeuf, p. 62. 'The German industrialist believes in organization, as he believes in Germany. He gives instructions and lets his subordinates act: to each his own job. Why should he do theirs?'

40. *BASF schreibt Geschichte* (1961), p. 9.

41. See p. 38.

42. Geigy, Sandoz, and CIBA have all published good firm histories in recent years.

See also the biography of Eduard Sandoz in: *Schweizer Pioniere der Wirtschaft und Technik*, 7 (1957), and the references cited on p. 21 on the development of the industry in Basle.

43. The Swiss chemical manufacturers were the most determined foes of a patent law in the last years of the 19th century. See p. 72.

44. *Ibid.*, p. 193. Even more than the Swiss, Solvay & Cie. of Belgium typifies this combination of traditional management and technical sophistication which seems inconsistent with conventional analyses of the family firm as a retardative factor in industrial growth. See L. F. Haber, pp. 191–192.

45. Péchiney was a pioneer in aluminum production by chemical means, but the head of the firm, A. R. Péchiney, refused to investigate Héroult's process for electrolytic reduction of alumina to the metal, claiming that the demand was and would remain totally inelastic. See M. Chêne, Industries savoyardes, *La Revue de Savoie* (1960), p. 26. When he did adopt the new process, at a place called Calypso, he is said to have commented that he kept a chorus girl, named Calypso, who ran to considerable money (*ibid.*, p. 28).

46. L. F. Haber, p. 113, summarizes the little that is known about this firm. V. K. Löffl, p. 177, states that annual dividends of around 10% were paid in 1909–1911.

47. *Schweizer Pioniere der Wirtschaft und Technik*, VII, p. 87.

48. The histories of French chemical firms are less informative than are the German, and especially the Swiss. The most important are: J. Choffel, *Saint–Gobain, du miroir à l'atome* (1960); J. Coignet, *Histoire de la Maison Coignet, 1818–1900* (1900); C. Gignoux, *Histoire d'une entreprise française* (1955), (about Péchiney); Kuhlmann, *Cent ans d'industrie chimique: Les Establissements Kuhlmann 1825–1925* (1926).

49. See A. Detoeuf, p. 68. 'He (the French industrialist) is without a rival in moderate-scale business, where the eye of the boss can see everything, but mediocre in big jobs where he must rely on others.'

50. A. Matagrin, p. 313. *BASF schreibt Geschichte*, p. 5. See below, p. 129.

51. St. Gobain statement from the *Rapports du Conseil d'Administration*, 1882. Brunck statement from *Die deutsche Industrie, Festgabe* vol. II, (1913), p. XXIa. It should not be inferred from the references to St. Gobain in connection especially with discussions of entrepreneurial mentality, that this company was especially conservative or technologically backward. The choice of St. Gobain is based on the fact that this was the only firm whose reports were available to me for this period. In fact St. Gobain was managed according to normal standards of prudence for French industry of this time. There is, indeed, reason to suppose that St. Gobain was technically more dynamic than the annual reports would lead one to believe. These reports illustrate not so much the behavior of the management as the standards and attitudes expected of prudent management by stockholders.

52. See A. Haller, *Les industries chimiques et pharmaceutiques. Exposition de Paris 1900* vol. I, (1903), p. LXXII; *Chimie et Industrie*, I (1910), pp. 554–555.

53. The following quote is translated from the 1874 report: 'keep a close watch,

without however letting ourselves be drawn into costly experiments, on the new chemical processes which appear so to speak all the time in the present state of Science, and which threaten to supplant the old methods.'

54. In 1866, St. Gobain hesitated to expand in chemicals because it was not a leader in this field, as opposed to glass, where it had to fear encroachment. It must be emphasized again that references to St. Gobain do not imply that it was more conservatively managed than other firms in the industry. The choice of examples is dictated by the availability of information. Furthermore, as already pointed out, the management probably invested more resources in research than they would admit to stockholders.

55. E. Grandmougin, *L'enseignement de la chimie industrielle* (1917), p. 8; E. Fleurent, I, p. 81.

56. The interpretation of the case as based on the lack of interest of Lyons dyers in a revolutionary change in their techniques is based on Laferrère, p. 161.

57. E. Bäumler, pp. 21–22.

58. D. Landes, Technological Change and Industrial Development in Western Europe, 1750–1914, p. 581. The present discussion was largely written before the appearance of this remarkable essay, and I have not attempted to do justice to the many points at which it touches on the problems relevant here.

59. J. Beer, p. 87.

4

Knowledge-centered firms in the chemical industry

1. Types of chemical firms

To round out Part I and the discussion of growth in the European chemical industry, we shall look briefly at the ways in which varying amounts of technical effort shaped the economic behavior of firms, and their interaction. For this purpose, it is convenient to abstract from the many enterprises and branches four representative types of chemical firm. They will be characterized by factor intensities, size of firm, product variety, importance of technical effort, location, and market structure[1]).

1.1. Heavy inorganics or 'Soda' producers

The typical firms in this sector were the British soda manufacturers, but similar characteristics were found in French and German companies, and in German and British tar distilleries as well as electrolytic plants on the continent. 'Soda' firms were capital-intensive, centering production around one or a few processes with fairly stable basic technology. By comparison to other chemical firms, relatively little research was carried out, though there was ample scope for engineering improvements and cost-cutting, particularly in materials handling. Firms and plants were large for the industry, producing a relatively narrow range of products. Location was determined by access to raw materials, energy, and water, which meant that transport was a major consideration. There were few firms in each national industry, and agreements limiting competition in important products were common. Sulfuric acid was produced in more scattered plants than other heavy chemicals, since it was widely used and particularly troublesome to transport. In relation to total capital or firm size, technical effort was least important in 'Soda' firms. In the early decades of the 20th century, inorganic producers turned to more sophisticated technology, involving new electrical or thermal processes. In France, the transition was triggered by the wartime emergency.

1.2. Specialties or 'Lyon' firms

Somewhat more knowledge-centered, in a pre-scientific way, were a large group of chemical enterprises making a varied range of products. It is difficult to say very much about this diverse and unspectacular branch of the industry. In many instances, the firms shaded off into activities not ordinarily considered chemical production, such as paints, inks, adhesives, abrasives, and cleaning compounds. We shall consider the so-called 'para-chemical' sector again in Part II, but as a customer of the chemical industry rather than a branch of it. Much of Lyons' chemical industry was of the specialties type, but it had numerous representatives elsewhere, in Paris for example, and in German industrial towns. Little capital was used, and firms were ordinarily small. Technical effort was relatively important, but neither very formalized nor highly scientific. Nonetheless, the technology usually protected only by secrecy, could be complex. Firms would have a few standard products, for which they were known suppliers, and supplement these with newly developed items, or goods for which a temporary market appeared. Markets might be local or wider, and could be described as monopolistically competitive. Urban or suburban locations predominated, meeting the need for easy access to labor and customers while providing adequately for modest space requirements.

1.3. Organic chemicals or 'Dyes' firms

Large-scale production of synthetic organic chemicals was the province of the great German dyestuffs manufacturers. Their activity was based on the application of chemical knowledge of an exact sort, but they were also capital-intensive, leading to high value-added per man as well as per unit of raw material. The location of these firms was determined by the availability of water, of transport, and of land on which to expand. Technical effort was on an impressive scale, in laboratories, pilot plants, and engineering workshops, and in the organization of production. The firms applied science not only to the development of new products and processes, but also to improving their inputs of materials and capital goods, and to developing the techniques of using their products. The firms were large, and the plants often very large indeed. There were only a few firms of any consequence in the field, though marginal producers with an entirely different type of operation persisted for some time. The large firms produced a wide range of output, and in some cases entered into price-regulating agreements, which were often of short duration. A more important trend than cartellization was concentration, with the *Interessen-gemeinschaft* (IG), or 'community of interests', as a step between independence and the formation of a trust.

1.4. Scientific specialties or 'Basle' firms

In Basle especially, but also in Germany, there were firms that resembled the 'Lyon' type in production and scale, but which were chemically even more sophisticated than the large dyestuffs houses. They produced synthetic organic chemicals, such as dyestuffs and pharmaceuticals, but specialized in difficult products where there were diseconomies of scale, or where research could provide a technical advantage in a product of relatively high value. As knowledge spread and grew, this meant abandoning products when they could be made cheaply and on a large scale. Location was conditioned by the presence of abundant water, by tradition in an urban area, and by transport. Research was important, with emphasis on the chemical laboratory rather than on engineering. As was true of the large organic firms, biological research was also carried out, since a part of the output was used in medicine or agriculture. Firms were of moderate size, and agreements with competitors and supplier firms in the heavy organics sector, though tried, were not stable. The high degree of specialization weakened the tendency toward trust formation, while allowing limited technical cooperation to exist side by side with competition.

In brief, the four types of chemical production characteristic of the pre-1914 period in Europe can be arranged in a two-way classification, using the amount of capital (say per man) as one indicator and the scope of technical effort as the other. This is done in Fig. 6.

2. Economic behavior of chemical firms

The degree to which technical considerations dominated the management of chemical firms, as shown for example by the role of technical men in management functions, varied in part with technical effort and in part with the importance of capital. The 'Dyes' firms applied exact knowledge

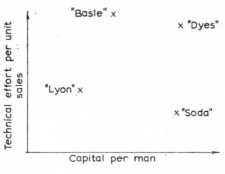

Fig. 6.

to most aspects of the business, including sales and production supervision. An outstanding and well-documented example is Duisberg's work
in organizing the Leverkusen plant of Bayer. The new plant was planned
from the ground up, with special concern for flexibility and standardization[2]). Yet the 'Basle' firms did not extend the emphasis on technical
effort which marked their research and sales departments to the production side[3]). French 'Soda' firms, on the other hand, did employ technical
supervisors and plant engineers. Although the men were not trained
chemical engineers, and could thus do little to improve technology, they
represented a distinct improvement over the traditional practice of putting
a 'retired policeman' in charge, as one writer put it[4]).

The economic incentive to large-scale production also depended on
factor proportions as well as on the role of technical effort. Capital-using
'Soda' and 'Dye' firms tended to be large and to have large plants. But
scale was particularly important for the latter, since production had to
finance technical effort, itself subject to economies of scale. The specialties manufacturers, on the other hand, restricted technical effort pretty
much to the laboratory, which made it cheaper. They also limited the
scope of their activity to a few products in which technical effort could
earn a high gross rent. In this way, even the most knowledge-centered
among them could remain of moderate size, while some 'Lyon' firms could
keep a small market in a few differentiated products with little pressure
from larger or more knowledge-centered competitors.

Location was conditioned largely by factor proportions and scale. As
we noted, heavy chemicals and dyes were made where transport, energy,

and water were freely available. Specialties firms retained urban locations, near workers and customers, which remained adequate for their needs[5]). In more recent times, technical effort has allowed chemical firms to adapt to a variety of locational patterns. The German predilection for size is reflected in huge establishments centralizing nearly all operations of even the largest firms, except for particular production facilities located elsewhere and field sales offices. Thus the BASF employed some 50 000 people in its Ludwigshafen plant in the early 1960s. French firms, on the other hand, follow a pattern more like American practice, with a variety of locations and divisions, including separate administration and research facilities. Chemical firms can also make their locational decisions responsive to public policy. It might be thought that knowledge-centered operation, with its increased requirements for information, would impose greater constraints on location and plant scale, but the opposite is true. Emphasis on information has led to great advances in handling it, so that almost any degree of centralization or separation is feasible, and tastes or particular circumstances dictate decisions in specific cases.

Virtually all chemical firms, and even individual plants, produced a number of products. From earliest times, chemical processes had given a mix of outputs, and early technical effort was often directed at finding uses for by-products. As the industry matured, product diversity became less a technical necessity and more the result of emphasis on technical effort. When a large part of the cost of production is the rent to technical effort, marginal cost is low, so that it pays a firm to continue making the product when demand falls off. Then, too, technical effort yields new ideas for products, and also makes for more carefully differentiated outputs to fill precisely defined needs. Finally, the range of products reflected the rapid pace of change characteristic of the more knowledge-centered firms.

It is in studying change in the chemical industry that the full significance of technical effort in shaping economic behavior and destiny emerges. The industry first showed its character in breaking away from the users whose auxiliary it had at first been. Where soda and dyestuffs had been made by textile finishers, in later years chemical firms operated dye works as application research facilities[6]). Although textile finishers, glass and soap makers, and other traditional customers remained large users of chemicals, change in the industry ceased to be a direct reflection of economic conditions in particular sectors. This was particularly true of 'Dyes' and 'Basle' firms, where the rhythm of progress was set by technical effort. Not only were economic responses to external change more rapid and smooth, but market changes provoked technical response, and the sources of profit were regenerated by new products, processes, and end-uses. 'Dyes' firms, for example, integrated backward and began to manufacture heavy chemicals when prices or qualities were not satisfactory. Bayer began to make sulfuric acid, whose price was controlled by a cartel, while the BASF developed the contact process for the same product when it required concentrated acid in great quantities[7]). 'Basle' firms, unable to compete directly with the large German *Konzern*, relied on self-generated innovations to sustain their market position. They could least of any be satisfactorily described by the traditional static model of maximization within a given technological constraint.

The idea that technical effort is the key to growth and profits made much slower headway in the 'Soda' and 'Lyon' firms. Yet the pressure of external change forced them, too, to make technical adjustments, particularly in the case of soda itself when the Solvay process threatened the Leblanc producers. There was indeed a technical response, in the form of a number of improvements to the old process. However, the relative lack of technical effort not only made adjustment more difficult, but prevented more radical changes either in technology or in the activity mix of the firms. The result was to limit their growth.

Knowledge-centered firms were able to grow almost independently of the prospects in particular markets. Products and uses changed, and the sources of profit changed even more rapidly. A survey of German chemical firms in 1893 showed that the highest dividends were paid by producers of organic chemicals, including explosives and specialties, and the lowest by manufacturers of inorganic chemicals and fertilizers[8]). Moreover, when new and more complex lines of business were contemplated, the stock of knowledge accumulated was a more valuable asset than capital, resources, or existing market positions. As an example, the French firms that went into the production of organic materials as a result of the wartime emergency began with the production of chlorine, a difficult material they had learned to handle, as the intermediate step to the new type of technology[9]). Chlorine was also the key to Griesheim Elektron's successful diversification from acids and fertilizer into electrolysis, organic chemicals, and complex metal specialty compounds[10]). More generally, technology was the dominant factor in the development of the electrochemical industry in Germany. Although capital was an important input, and the electrical industry had closer connections to banks than the chemical, it was the latter that played the leading role. The AEG electrical company, one of Germany's 'big two', sold its electrochemical interests to Griesheim[11]).

In summary, although knowledge-centered firms did not have to be large, they were enabled to grow by relying on continued and substantial technical effort. Relatively backward firms were subject to pressure on profits from the steady fall in chemical prices, and from their comparative inflexibility in products and processes. Knowledge-centered firms, on the other hand, had less stable profits for particular operations, owing to the uncertain and delayed returns from technical effort, but their overall profit picture was much more favorable. Diversity evened out the particular fluctuations, and the overall level and trend of profits were higher. Whereas 'Soda' firms stress conditions in user industries in explaining bad years, a 'Dyes' firm feels the pinch of a crisis year in the difficulties it faces in selling new shares[12]).

3. The knowledge-centered industry

Knowledge-centered and backward firms coexisted in the European chemical industry before 1914, but the former grew faster and represented a growing fraction of the total. When backward, or relatively backward firms survived, it was either due to protection, as in the case of higher-cost French soda, or because they retained small or specialized markets that their aggressive competitors ignored. In addition, there was a steady increase in technical effort in the 'Soda' and 'Lyon' type of firms, which could use the knowledge becoming available from within and without industry, and which were forced to accept more stringent technical standards by competitive pressure. Thus it can be said that the chemical industry was becoming knowledge-centered as a whole. Not only were the knowledge-centered firms increasingly important, particularly if one uses profits rather than sales as the criterion, but example and competition increased the role of technical effort in those of the others who survived.

Because of product differentiation, economies of scale, and the transitory nature of the return to technical effort, a knowledge-centered industry could not be truly competitive. Short-run monopoly positions were common. In addition, producers might enjoy a monopoly position so long as they did not try to exploit their power to the full, or the attack might come in the form of a near-substitute rather than a new source of the same product. The characteristic feature of the industry was the existence of more potential than actual producers, as in the case of the Swiss, who broke the 1881 Alizarin Convention between German producers, then gave up manufacturing the dye when prices fell again. On the one hand, the industry seemed monopolistic, because prices included a return to technical effort, and were therefore above marginal cost. On the other hand, technical effort gave firms an extra dimension of response to the opportunities created by monopoly, even when protected by secrecy or patents. The inherent instability of market positions meant that it was even rational for firms to use profits to finance technical effort that would undermine their own position.

One notable exception to the fragility of monopoly in chemicals was the German *Kalisyndikat*, or potash trust, which controlled the European market for this fertilizer until World War I. Because of the reluctance of agriculture to adopt new inputs and change its techniques, the syndicate was required to engage in technical effort and to offer its output at favorable prices.

Market restriction short of monopoly was commonly tried, especially in standard products such as superphosphates, sulfuric acid, and soda, but it was not highly successful[13]). There were also mergers and consolidations in the inorganics sector, particularly in capital-intensive sectors where prices were falling[14]). In the 'Dyes' and 'Basle' sectors, the movement toward concentration was strengthened by the inherent difficulty in achieving any market stability in other ways. Knowledge-centered operation did not make for the quiet life. High profits were necessary to finance future technical effort, but they encouraged entry. As we have seen, it was impossible to organize stable cartels, since potential producers could not all be included.

In order to cope with these difficulties, firms entered into a series of agreements providing for sharing of profits and technical information. Later they formed closer relationships of the 'community-of-interests' or *Interessengemeinschaft* type[15]). There were advantages from a pooling of knowledge and of facilities, the latter especially for foreign sales and manufacturing operations, but the sharing of profits according to a rigid formula did not work out well, so that the formula of association with continued independence of operation led to difficulties. In the German case the solution was increasing amalgamation, culminating in a final merger in 1925, while the Swiss restored the *status quo ante* of independent firms, with limited cooperation in foreign operations and some specific technical problems.

As in the case of price agreements, other limited forms of cooperation between firms, such as cross-licensing, sharing of knowledge, co-ventures or an *Interessengemeinschaft*, were not regarded as substitutes for technical change, but rather as means to facilitate it. The basic innovation was that research no longer represented a reaction to danger, but the central growth-ensuring activity of the firm. In negotiations leading to agreements, the bargaining power of the firm depended to a large extent on its technical contribution or position[16]). And in return these agreements, by providing stability to the firm, gave it an opportunity to gain further strength.

Notes

1. For recent economic studies of the chemical industry from the French and German viewpoint, respectively, see: M. Lagache, *L'économie des industries chimiques* (1962); and P. Riebel, Chemische Industrie, in: *Handbuch der Sozialwissenschaften* (1959), II, pp. 492–505.
2. H. J. Flechtner, *Carl Duisberg,* pp. 142–143.
3. A. Bürgin, *Geigy,* p. 193.
4. M. Fauque, *L'évolution économique de la grande industrie chimique en France,* pp. 157 ff.
5. M. Laferrère, Les industries chimiques de la région lyonnaise, *Revue de Géographie de Lyon,* XXVII, *3* (1952), pp. 219–256.
6. N. Jaquet, *Die Entwicklung und volkswirtschaftliche Bedeutung der schweizerischen Teerfarbenindustrie* (1923), pp. 8–9; *Rundschau* (CIBA), no. 126 (May 1956), p. 46.
7. For the Bayer case, see C. Duisberg, *Meine Lebenserinnerungen,* p. 79.
8. A. Haller, *L'industrie chimique,* p. 32.
9. R. Guglielmo, *La grande industrie chimique en France* (1957), II, p. 41.
10. *75 Jahre chemische Fabrik Griesheim Elektron.*
11. C. Christiansen, Chemische- und Farbenindustrie, in: A. Weber, ed., *Über den Standort der Industrien,* II, 2 (1914), p. 33.
12. St. Gobain, *Rapports, passim,* but especially 1874–78, 1900, 1903; E. Bäumler, *Ein Jahrhundert Chemie,* p. 369.

Full bibliographical data are given in the Bibliography at the end of the book.

13. Thus the German acid cartel of the 1890s succeeded in causing Bayer to set up their own acid plant. Duisberg, *Lebenserinnerungen*, p. 79. For a description of the French superphosphate cartel, dominated by St. Gobain, see F. Laur, *De l'acca-parement*, III, pp. 229–307.

14. Examples are the formation of the United Alkali Company in England, and the absorption of fertilizer producers by St. Gobain. See, respectively, L. F. Haber, p. 180; St. Gobain, *Rapports*, 1895, 1899.

15. On the origins of I. G. Farben, see H. Wickel, *I.G. Deutschland: Ein Staat im Staate*(1932); F. ter Meer, *Die I.G. Farben* (1953). On the Basle I.G., see A. Bürgin, p. 246; *Sandoz, 1886–1961* (1961), p. 124. The Basle I.G. was not formally begun until 1918.

16. An example is the agreement between Agfa and Bayer on the Kongorot dyes after patent litigation. See H. J. Flechtner, *Carl Duisberg*, pp. 80–81.

The chemical industry and economic growth

5

The role of the chemical industry:
search for an approach

1. Introduction

Part II of this book is concerned with 'the economic significance' of the chemical industry in Europe between 1850 and 1914, the quotes recalling the rather empty title of many industry studies[1]). As we shall see, it is necessary to do some spade work before we can reach even the possibility of a meaningful answer. To begin with, we shall use economic growth as the dependent variable, i.e., as the yardstick for gauging the influence of of the chemical industry. Such a choice hardly needs justification in view of the intellectual climate of economics today, but it is by no means the only one that might have been made. We could have considered the role of the chemical industry in mobilizing a politically conscious proletariat, in hastening or retarding urbanization, in favoring or hindering distributive justice, or in relation to other social goals and results of economic activity.

Given our concern with growth, which in the given context is very nearly equivalent to industrialization or development, it is not clear that the 'role' of a particular industry need be investigated. Having studied the forces leading to growth in the industry, we can either add this evidence to other work on the sources of growth or retardation, or simply say that forces acting on one particular branch probably affected industry or the economy in general in similar ways. The difficulty with such an approach is that there is interaction between parts of the economy, in historical change as well as in the technical relationships set out in input–output tables. Moreover, it is not enough to say that everything depends on everything else. In order to achieve growth, or to explain it, we must reduce the web of causal factors and mechanisms to a sufficient minimum. Let us consider a hypothetical example. Suppose that growth depends on capital and entrepreneurship. The problem is to allocate these two scarce resources so as to maximize total growth. If sectors do not interact, the answer lies in equalizing the marginal return (in terms of sectoral growth) to both factors in all uses. With interaction, such a solution is inappropriate and total growth becomes the criterion. In the absence of suitable empirical evidence concerning the total growth achievable with different allocations, it is necessary to investigate directly the relationships between sectors for clues about the indirect effects of growth in particular ones.

The above, of course, is the problem of balanced or unbalanced growth, that overworked staple of development economics. The argument for concentrated growth rests largely on economies of scale, but it can also be based on the idea that certain types of economic activity have considerable growth-promoting effects. It then follows that the social rate of return in this industry is higher than the private rate. Furthermore, if the growth-promoting effects are due to particular resources, these in turn have a value to the economy that is understated by the market. In the pages that follow, we shall examine a number of possible mechanisms for transmitting growth. They will be tested for their logical validity and for their empirical relevance to the European chemical industry and its historical context.

It may seem presumptuous to speak of testing hypotheses with so little quantitative data, but the mechanisms involved are largely not amenable to precise measurement. For example, while it would be possible to test the hypothesis that an economy grows faster when its chemical industry grows faster, this would make no sense, since one expects the rate of growth of a part to be correlated with that of the whole. The effects the chemical industry may have had on the process of economic growth are of second order, and therefore require a more delicate approach.

Development theory abounds in empty economic boxes. The one marked 'leading sectors', to use but one of many labels, has a particularly elusive content, and yet can hardly be dispensed with so long as resources are scarce and imperfectly divisible. The object here is to specify channels in which growth impulses may flow, so that promising foci of growth can be identified. I shall not try to decide the question as to the precise magnitude of the chemical industry's influence, nor claim or deny the 'leading sector' label. Intuition and the literature accord the chemical industry some nontrivial role in economic growth. I shall assume they are correct and concentrate on mechanisms[2]).

2. The importance of chemical production in static terms

The simplest measure of a sector's importance to an economy is its size. On this showing, there is little to be said for concentrating on the chemical industry. Abstracting from the many and vexing problems of measurement and definition, no estimates of the industry's relative size put it at so much as 5% of all industry for either France or Germany. The data cited in Chapter 2 suggest that for France chemical production represented some 2% of value added in industry, while for Germany, employment in chemicals grew from 1.3% to 2.5% of all industry between 1875 and 1913. On a somewhat stricter definition of the industry, one perhaps more appropriate to the present study, the chemical industry in 1907 occupied some 0.6% of workers in industry in France, and 1.3% in Germany[3]). Clearly, any significant linkage effects from chemicals to the rest of the economy must have been relatively independent of size.

A familiar argument for showing the importance of a branch of production is to point out that its products are used widely. The implication is that the process of economic production and consumption would be severely crippled without them. Related to this are considerations about strategic materials and operations in connection with wartime production. The first class of arguments is characteristic of Anglo-Saxon apologias for science and industry, while the second stems from German strivings for autarkic security. Both are *ceteris paribus*, but the strategic goods view is explicitly concerned with short-run dislocations owing to war or blockade. In recent times development economists have stressed social overhead capital as irreplaceable in the growth process, while heavy industry has been accorded a special place in socialist economies and in the plans of developing nations. There is no doubt that to remove suddenly all chemicals (or any other class of industrial goods) would cause considerable dislocation, but this is not logically equivalent to the proposition that something like the same degree of economic productivity could not have been achieved with much less development of the particular branch. The fixed-proportions input–output model implicit in many 'key sector' arguments is not appropriate to long-term growth problems.

Even if one grants that chemical products and processes contribute substantially in the twentieth century to the complex industrial technology whose high productivity we enjoy, progress in the 19th century appears to have been less critical from this point of view. The basic chemicals produced in 1914 were known and available in quantity in 1850. Where they were not, as in the case of synthetic dyestuffs and medicinals, natural products were a partial substitute, and even their absence would not have had drastic consequences for industrial production. Furthermore, for any given country there was no need to make these products at home, as is shown by the fact that the largest users of synthetic dyestuffs – Great Britain, France, Japan, and the United States – imported the bulk of their supplies. Perhaps the most important new *products* introduced during the period were chemical fertilizers. But here as elsewhere, chemical progress did not come in response to bottlenecks, so that one cannot view chemical products as a critical piece in the puzzle of European industrial growth.

Development economists have singled out one unique 'commodity' that may be critical for growth, namely foreign exchange. Did the chemical industry provide the European economies with such generalized purchasing power? Surprisingly, even the German chemical industry was of limited importance as an exporter. In 1908, for example, chemicals represented 3.6% of German merchandise exports, while the corresponding figures for France and Switzerland were 2.4% and 3.7% respectively [4]). Of the three, France was the only one that imported more goods classified as chemicals than it exported, but the imports in all instances contained a high proportion of raw materials, and so are poor indicators of the importance of foreign supply for chemical manufacture. Two other qualifications concerning the data need to be made. A considerable fraction of foreign trade, particularly in sulfuric acid, was in fact local trade in border regions. And the Germans and Swiss both produced dyestuffs abroad, in tariff factories, to which they sent nearly finished goods. It was in the clear interest of the manufacturers to understate the value of the goods-in-transit (or overstate the value-added abroad) for tariff purposes. Thus, the German and Swiss exports are probably understated, and so, too, are the French imports.

It is fortunate that we can pass over the importance of the chemical industry as a source of foreign exchange, since economic historians of growth in 19th-century western Europe have placed almost no stress on bottlenecks in foreign exchange or the capacity to import. Protection is alleged to have hurt France by raising costs and sheltering inefficient industries, and to have helped Germany by sheltering infant industries and stimulating improved productivity to compensate for increased costs. Switzerland relied more on foreign trade, as its size would lead one to predict. Chemical exports were necessary for the German and Swiss producers to achieve sufficient scale. But any direct effects in the other direction, from chemicals to trade were small.

There remains the special problem of war. In 1914, France (and Britain) found that reliance on imports in the organic sector created a bottleneck in the supply of munitions, while Germany was able to adapt to the Allied blockade largely because of existing capacity and technology in nitrates, sulfur, fibers, drugs, and various *Ersatz* materials. A major factor in Germany's short-run advantage was the 'installed capacity' for technical effort, and it was a rapid increase in this activity on the part of the Allies that enabled them to catch up part way.

3. Chemicals and derived demand

Linkage effects have commonly been understood to operate by means of mechanisms involving derived demand. Growth in one sector leads to demand for a variety of purchased inputs, raw materials as well as intermediate products, and this transmits the stimulus for growth to the affected industries. To begin with, such a mechanism implies a Keynesian, or demand-oriented, view of economic growth in industrializing countries. We shall return to this point, but there is a more elementary one to be made. The strength of derived demand flowing from one portion of the economy depends on its size and its rate of growth. Now, in the early and presumably uncertain stages of growth it is usually true that the two dimensions are inversely related, i.e., rapidly growing sectors are small. This was the dilemma confronting Marczewski when he tried to test the Rostovian growth mechanism, using preliminary data for France[5]). The phenomenon is logically predictable: if one is considering an economy not yet fully caught up in modern growth, as the term 'leading sector' suggests, it is implausible to think of rapid growth taking place in so substantial a part of the economy that all or most of the rest is pulled along within a short time-span. The derived growth model is suitable to a Keynesian world in which the inducement to invest is the growth-limiting factor. Here, an autonomous rise in demand (for example, a housing or durable goods boom) leads to a cumulative process of increased activity and growth. Looked at in this way, the stimulus comes not only from derived demand for goods but also from the income generated by payments to labor and capital. The importance of leverage is brought out if one considers the income multiplier effects.

In any case, the weight of the chemical industry, even adjusted for its rate of growth relative to industry in general, was small in 19th-century Europe. If we take the data already used, the share of chemicals in German industry averaged 2% (using employment as the measure), and its rate of growth was twice that of industry as a whole, so that its 'growth-weight' might be considered the product of the two, or 4%. The French data are a bit less stable, but yield a similar weight for the later 19th century, somewhat less for the period from 1850 to 1875[6]).

Despite the limited relevance of the derived-demand mechanism for the chemical industry, it is worth pursuing a bit further in search of a more precise understanding of linkage effects. There is one demand-led model of development that is highly regarded because it appears to fit the classic case of industrialization, that of Britain. It is commonly held that *the* Industrial Revolution was triggered by a boom in exports in the later 18th century, centered on, though not limited to, cotton textiles. It is neither within the scope of this book nor within my competence to argue the case. I merely note that the export-led model requires the assumption that a substantial portion of the British economy had high elasticity of supply. Such appears in fact to have been the case at least for industrial labor, food, certain other wage goods, and capital goods. Another way of expressing the assumption is to say that the English economy had such strong external economies that an exogenous demand push led to growth and increasing returns to scale on a virtually economy-wide basis.

A model such as the above makes no allowance for abortive starts, or for beginnings that lead to slow or unsteady growth. An alternative approach to the problem of transition to modern growth is to focus on supply, and suggest that inelasticities are the characteristic feature of the non-growing economy. Now the mechanism of derived demand looks even more problematical. Not only is the response (quantity supplied or demanded) small for a given stimulus (shift in the demand or supply schedule of the 'leading' industry), but the continued growth of the leader is itself threatened by inadequate supply conditions and the absence of demand to supplement the exogenous source. On this showing, a high rate of growth in any sizeable industry accompanied by substantial derived

economic activity in other branches, argues for the existence of a progressive economy rather than saying much about the particular industry.
To be sure, growth is never precisely uniform throughout the economy,
and it may in fact be highly concentrated in one or several branches for a
time. But to call such branches leading sectors is non-operational. In the
context of purposive development, it is a dangerous example of *post hoc,
ergo propter hoc*, and may lead to serious misallocation. There are also
examples of rapid growth in part of an economy that is clearly not progressive, such as export enclaves and modern urban-industrial complexes
in backward economies. Their characteristic property is that they *minimize* linkage effects, precisely because the backward economy would
choke off their growth by its sluggish response. In the export enclave case
linkages may be very nearly zero, while in the other type of partial growth
they consist mainly of resource transfers (labor, food, export earnings)
from the backward to the modern sector.

Returning to the chemical industry, I conclude that it did not exert any
great influence on growth by stimulating the demand for other products,
or, more generally, by raising the level of economic activity. It can be
added that this result is predictable from simple economic reasoning,
which might go without saying in the absence of the considerable con-
fusion surrounding the subject.

The historical evidence turns up a number of instances in which particular factors of production or industrial branches were stimulated by
market linkages from the chemical industry, but there are also cases where
chemicals substituted for other materials and led to less activity, i.e., the
freeing of resources. Before reviewing some specific cases, a comment on
the last clause is in order. Note that decreased activity is equivalent to
freed resources, yet one would normally think of the two phenomena as
opposite in respect of their effect on economic growth. Again, it depends
on the model used. In the Keynesian view, demand is the limiting factor.
Resources are unemployed at the margin and more activity is likely to
lead to growth. In the classical view, it is resources that are scarce and an
activity that frees them contributes to growth. The remainder of the book
focuses on productivity, and thus chooses the classical or neo-classical
view. However, in a Malthusian economy, as the French call it, an industry may retard growth by means of the same effects which are favorable
in a progressive environment. This is one possible meaning of the paradox

that the greatest force making for economic growth is growth itself.

Chemical production used large quantities of natural resources, but where the industry was a leading user, they seldom had high opportunity cost. A salient characteristic of the industry was that it used cheap or formerly useless materials to replace scarce ones. Examples are pyrites and later gypsum for sulfur, lignite and poor coal for tar, and remote hydro-electric energy used for chemicals where it was produced. Usually, direct chemical use was only the first step, and other materials were made available as by-products. In the case of pyrites, the metallic part of the ores was recovered. In Germany, twelve acid manufacturers founded the 'Duis-berger Kupferhütte' in 1876 to centralize the purchase, roasting, and beneficiation of pyrites. At first they recovered chiefly copper, silver, gold, and iron, but after World War I the company became a supplier of cobalt, lead, zinc, and tin as well[7]). Chemical processes requiring cheap energy were located near lignite fields permitting the use of this low-grade fuel[8]). Similarly, the value of marginal coal deposits was enhanced by the development of by-product coking, which yielded usable coke as well as tar and other materials from inferior coal[9]). Chemical uses, and the locational flexibility of the industry played a large part in permitting hydroelectric power to be developed more quickly than progress in transmitting current would otherwise have allowed. In more recent times, the production of chemicals has been used to absorb seasonal peaks of power production[10]).

The demand for manufactured inputs to the chemical industry did not become important until the end of the period under discussion, when chemical processes involving high temperatures and pressures were introduced. Before this time one finds the beginnings of an engineering industry in Basle with a significant part of the demand coming from the chemical industry[11]). The chemical industry was also an early user of refrigeration equipment, second in time only to food processing, and specializing in large and complex units[12]).

The demand of the chemical industry for labor was not a significant factor in the aggregate, though it was a leading employer in certain local markets, such as Mannheim–Ludwigshafen, the Alpine valleys of France, and a number of smaller towns. There were also incidental and diverse effects on the structure of the demand for labor in particular places. For example, while the chemical activity centered on Lyons contributed to the development of artificial textiles employing female rural workers, in

Ludwigshafen the emphasis on male labor in the BASF created a need for new industries employing a high proportion of women[13]). Technically trained manpower was obviously much more affected by the chemical industry than was industrial labor in general, but it is best to put off discussion of this factor of production until the next chapter.

Natural dyestuffs, some medicinal products, and other materials as well were displaced by cheap synthetic products with a consequent decrease in net activity (or a net freeing of resources). It should be noted, however, that the new production was seldom located in the same country as the old, much less in the same locality, so that the gross effects were locally drastic in the short run, as in Provence and Alsace when alizarin displaced madder.

4. The chemical industry and economic efficiency

It is clearly time to draw on the major premise of this study concerning economic growth, and on the concurring results of Part I. Improvements in productivity are far more important to economic growth than increases in the amount of resources engaged in production. For a given productive function, an industry's contribution to the efficiency of the economy is inversely rather than directly related to its claim on scarce resources. Over time, the direct contribution is given by the elasticity of supply, where the supply schedule can be thought of as the locus of price-quantity points over time. We use this long-run 'supply curve' to reflect both market response and technical change, in line with the analysis in Chapter 3.

If the factors of production receive the same return in all uses, then rapid gains in productivity in one industry must be reflected in falling relative prices. The general trend of industrial prices was regularly downward for the period under consideration in both France and Germany. Taking 1913 as 100, the mid-19th-century price index in France was about 140 for all industry (including mining and construction) on a value-added basis, and 119 on a gross sales basis[14]). Unfortunately, the overall price data for chemicals are not usable. Yet it is clear that European chemical prices fell more rapidly than the general average of industrial prices. Table 4 gives some examples of price behavior in chemicals. Two features stand out: the drastic downward changes over short periods following the introduction of a major innovation, and the persistent fall in prices of products with established technology, owing to supposedly

Table 4. Price behavior of selected chemicals.

Commodity	Year	Price	Unit and place	Comment	Source
Phosphorus	1821	90	fr/kg France	1838–1846: Production for use in matches begun.	Coignet (1900) p. 28
	1838	24			
	1839	12			
	1840	8.5			
	1879	5			
Soda	1855	650–700	fr/ton France	1873: Solvay process introduced	Association Nationale d'Expansion Economique, *Enquête sur la production française et la concurrence étrangère* (1917) Lambert, 'Engrais...' p. 112.
	1864–68	300			
	1874–78	280			
	1884–88	120			
	1892–96	110			
	1900–05	100			
	1910–14	100		1900 (about) Leblanc dies out in France.	
Sulfuric Acid	1898	11	fr/100 kg 66° Bé France		Fauque (1932) pp. 32–33.
	1913	7.75			
Chlorine	1880	37.6	fr/100 kg France	Weldon process Weldon-Péchiney process Deacon process	Gignoux (1955) p. 52.
	1887	17			
	1889	7.7			
Benzol	1887–1890	3	shillings/gallon (average) Great Britain	Germans began scrubbing benzol from coke gas 1890	Haber (1958) Appendix 3
	1900–1908	1			
Indigo	1895	35	fr/kg France	First synthetic indigo sold 1897	Lambert (1917) p. 139
	1913	10			
Synthetic dyes	1870	1500–1800	Mk/100 kg (average)		Redlich (1914) p. 45.
	1896	400			

minor improvements. The latter effect, which reflects continuing technical effort, was probably more important for growth since it applied to products with sizeable sales.

Even price data do not give a full picture of the lowered costs made possible by progress in chemicals. Since chemicals are used as inputs to other production processes, the relevant price is not that of the good, but the cost of performing a particular function in the latter process. Price indices do not adequately reflect quality changes, greater uniformity, new grades, and new products, and so do not reveal the savings made possible. For example, Solvay soda was purer than the Leblanc product[15]). Similarly, the index of dyestuff prices in Table 4 fails to take into account that the dyes of 1912 were much more versatile and economical in use than of 1896, and *a fortiori* than the few synthetics available in 1870[16]).

A characteristic of the chemical industry was its search for new markets, the technical implications of which will be examined later. But an aggressive price policy was part of the picture[17]). In established lines, the large tonnages involved and the wide variety of users made continued low prices a significant factor in lowering costs[18]). Finally, lower costs for one type of chemical were reflected in the prices of others, since the several branches of the industry had close ties. The chemical industry has traditionally been its own best customer.

Cheap chemicals had effects on other industries, though their magnitude is hard to evaluate, and even their direction is not always clear-cut. Let us consider textiles as an example. On the one hand, cheap synthetic dyes increased the income elasticity of demand for textiles by making possible frequent changes in fashion[19]). Not only were the dyes cheaper, but they made piece-dyeing possible. This lowered the price of colored fabrics, but it also hurt the business of those, such as the Lyons silk weavers, who had previously commanded a high return for their skill. Their patterned fabrics could not compete with solid-colored cloth. The expected reaction on the part of Lyons entrepreneurs, namely rapid mechanization of the weaving process, was not forthcoming. It may be that the shift away from patterns was too rapid, but in any case falling demand retarded change[20]). The silk men of Lyons seem to have suffered from the 'Arkansas Traveler' syndrome: he would not fix his leaking roof when it rained, and the roof did not leak any other time. The Mulhouse calico printers also found that the simplifications in printing made possible by the use of synthetic dyes reduced their special advantage[21]).

Less well-placed textile manufacturers, on the other hand, obtained advantages as they adopted the advances made possible by chemicals. Wool manufacture in northern and eastern France was stimulated, and the Swiss were encouraged to upgrade the quality of their textiles[22]). But the major effect of easy mechanization and cheap competition for high-skill products undoubtedly took place outside the industrial heartland. Chemicals played their part in enabling non-European countries to begin industrializing, especially in textiles.

When we look at foreign trade, pretty clearly cheap chemicals helped and dear ones hurt. At least the free-trading Mulhouse printers complained that the British derived much of their advantage from cheap inorganic chemicals and no tariffs on dyestuffs. The protectionists from the spinning and weaving branches in Normandy and the North maintained a discreet silence on the role of tariffs in raising their costs, stressing rather taxes and insufficient social overhead capital[23]). But then in most branches, textile finishing being an exception, chemicals represented a small part of total costs, so that differences in price between home and abroad could be of only limited significance. The leverage problem is involved here, as in the case of derived demand. Nonetheless, textiles were a low-margin industry, for the most part, and some writers could claim that chemical prices made a difference[24]).

Germany's comparative advantage in chemicals was not primarily due to price, although low prices helped her producers retain a near monopoly in organic chemicals up to the war. But German coal became competitive with British in part owing to chemical developments, namely the development of by-product coking. Whether this was really the critical step in bringing the whole heavy industry complex up to the British level, as one writer claims, cannot be established, nor can one be sure what influence the absence of a local dyestuff industry had on the failure of the British to adopt the new method[25]). Timing may have been important here: the Germans reacted sensitively and rapidly to the rise in tar prices by developing by-product coking, and the British, faced with a market already lost in part, now had little incentive to undertake massive investments in order to increase their output of tar.

The chemical industry supplied a growing variety of products in ever greater quantities and at falling prices. With the exception of technically trained manpower, it made few demands on scarce resources, while its products and the structure of its demand for inputs raised the value of existing raw materials or replaced them with more abundant substitutes. Chemicals were the very opposite of a growth-blocking industry, but since the absence of bottlenecks is less spectacular than their presence, we are left with the paradox that a major contribution of chemicals was their continued peacetime anonymity. Yet on the basis of the evidence reviewed so far, we can at most grant the industry a permissive rather than a propulsive role in economic growth. Not only is there little evidence of spectacular gains to the economy from growth in chemicals, but we have not yet found even a theoretical possibility of true 'leading sector' behavior on the part of a small industry. The major leverage problem would be attenuated in the case of a larger industry, but then the strength of response from the rest of the economy would be critical. Even continued growth of the single sector might require an economy so responsive as to be capable of growth without any particular push from a leading sector.

It should be noted that where the chemical industry contributed most to growth in terms of the effects considered above, it was nearly always due to some result of knowledge-centered operation. Technical change was responsible for continued price declines, for products cheaper to use as well as to buy, and for rapid adjustment to special situations in raw material supply. In the next chapter, we shall examine other and more far-reaching ways in which technical effort enabled the chemical industry to play a significant role in European economic growth.

Notes

1. Studies of the 19th century chemical industry, despite their titles, are of relatively little help. More has been done for recent times, but even then few analytic treatments exist. In addition to the sources in Ch. 1, see: M. Dumas, Le progrès dans l'industrie chimique, *Cahiers de l'ISEA*, no. 123 (March 1962); Deutschland's chemische Industrie, *Chemische Industrie*, iv, 10 (October 1952); W. Koeck, Die volkswirtschaftliche Funktion der Chemie, *Der Volkswirt*, no. 14 (Supplement, April 1954).
2. W. W. Rostow, *The Stages of Economic Growth* (1960), p. 59, includes chemicals in the list of leading sectors after 1875. See also R. Richeux, *L'industrie chimique en*

Full bibliographical data are given in the Bibliography at the end of the book.

France (1958), p. 9 and M. Dumas, *Le progrès dans l'industrie chimique* (1912), p. 7, for expressions of this feeling.

3. Industry here includes mining and construction. The subsectors covered are as follows, Germany: heavy chemicals, specialties, pharmaceuticals, dyestuffs, fertilizers; France: inorganic chemicals, organic chemicals, pharmaceuticals.

   The approximate absolute numbers are, Germany: 138 000 people; France: 40 000. Various subsectors sometimes included in the industry have been omitted, for example, soap, fats, explosives, and gasworks. Sources: *Annuaire statistique de la France, 1909*, pp. 188, 189. *Statistisches Jahrbuch für das deutsche Reich, 1909*, pp. 75, 76.

4. Sources: for France, *Annuaire statistique de la France, 1909*, pp. 237–238; for Germany, *Statistisches Jahrbuch für das deutsche Reich, 1909*, pp. 153, 154ff.; for Switzerland, *Annuaire statistique de la Suisse, 1949*, pp. 282, 302.

5. J. Marczewski, Y a-t-il eu un 'take-off' en France?, *Cahiers de l'ISEA*, no. 111 (March 1961).

6. Data from W. G. Hoffmann (1965) and T. J. Markovitch, respectively. See note 2, Ch. 1.

7. See the company history, *75 Jahre Duisburger Kupferhütte, 1875–1951, passim*; also R. B. Pilcher and F. Butler-Jones, *What Industry Owes to Chemical Science* (1918), pp. 28–30.

8. M. Baumont, *La grosse industrie allemande et le lignite* (1928), pp. 109–112. Other main users were sugar refining and potash.

9. See M. Baumont, *La grosse industrie allemande et le charbon* (1928), p. 30. The parallel with France, where the failure to adopt the new technique of destructive distillation with by-product recovery has been attributed to the lack of good coking coal, is interesting. After World War I with the birth, or rebirth, of the French organic industry, coke production increased rapidly.

10. V. Barut, *L'industrie de l'électrochimie et de l'électrométallurgie en France* (1924), p. 232.

11. See A. Bruckner, ed., *Wirtschaftgeschichte Basel* (1947), *passim*; H. Schwabe, ed., *Schaffendes Basel: 2000 Jahre Basler Wirtschaft* (1957), p. 196.

12. Linde, *50 Jahre Kältetechnik, 1879–1929* (1929), pp. 36–39, 85, 186.

13. See, respectively, M. Laferrère, *Lyon*, p. 428; and E. Plewe, Die Bedeutung der Industrie von Mannheim–Ludwigshafen, *BASF Works Magazine* (1955), no. 4, p. 166.

14. T. J. Markovitch, Appendix, table 5a.

15. Solvay, *Soude et produits chimiques* (1889), p. 43.

16. C. Ungewitter, *Chemie in Deutschland* (1938), p. 15, speaks of the characteristic cheapening in use with synthetic materials.

17. See W. Koeck, Die volkswirtschaftliche Funktion der Chemie, *Der Volkswirt*, Supplement to no. 14 (April 1954), p. 38.

18. See A. Binz, *Ursprung und Entwicklung der chemischen Industrie* (1910), p. 6.

19. M. Laferrère, p. 114; H. Caro, *Ueber die Entwicklung der Teerfarbenindustrie* (1893), p. 92.

20. M. Laferrère, pp. 127–130.
21. *Histoire documentaire de l'industrie de Mulhouse* (1902), pp. 337–338.
22. *Dix ans d'efforts* (1926), p. 145; *Histoire documentaire de Mulhouse* (1902), p. 335.
23. *Enquête parlementaire sur le régime économique*, I (1870), *passim*.
24. See: *Dix ans d'efforts* (1926), p. 1423; and also E. Grandmougin (1919), p. 259, who gives the figure of 1 % for the cost of dyestuffs in total sales of textiles, but nevertheless stresses the role of high duties on these materials.
25. H. Schall, *Die chemische Industrie Deutschlands* (1959), p. 99.

6

The chemical industry
and transmitted technical progress

When we considered how improved productivity in the chemical industry stimulated growth in other areas of the economy, it turned out that the most powerful effect was not due to falling prices in given products, but to the impact of new products. To take the example of synthetic dyes and textiles, the stimulus came primarily from the possibility of dyeing woven cloth rapidly and uniformly, and of changing from block to cylinder printing[1]). The contribution of the chemical industry came not so much from the efficiency with which it made chemicals as from the productivity of the chemicals it made. In turn, chemical products were productive less because they performed given tasks more efficiently, though they did that as well, than because they enlarged the spectrum of technical possibilities open to other industries.

New products implied new knowledge. It was necessary to discover and analyze needs or to prospect potential uses for a discovery. Then there was the knowledge embodied in developing and manufacturing the product. Finally, while an innovation might open up possibilities for changing non-chemical technology, the possibilities had to be elaborated and effectively applied. Technical effort made the chemical industry a valuable source of knowledge for the European economies, as I shall try to show in this chapter. Not only was the amount of knowledge produced large, but much of it was relevant to the economic needs of other industries, in addition to ensuring growth in chemicals themselves. We shall examine successively the new materials made available, the external applications of chemical techniques, the direct concern of chemical companies in improving other technologies, and the example of knowledge-centered operation provided by the industry.

There are two reasons for believing that the flow of knowledge will prove to be a fruitful mechanism for analyzing intersectoral influences.

The role of greater productivity in growth needs no restatement here, and knowledge sets the limits of economic efficiency. In addition, the vexing problem of leverage largely disappears. Knowledge is a public good in the sense that it is not exhausted by use. The value of a new dye to the textile industry, or of a new fertilizer to agriculture, depended on the improvement in productivity made possible and on the size of the activity enjoying the improved technique. So long as there was no bottleneck in making the chemical, the size of the chemical industry and the small amount which might be spent on the particular product were irrelevant.

If the flow of knowledge is going to be the key to explaining growth stimuli, then the relevance of our earlier emphasis on technical effort and the workings of the knowledge-centered firm should become clear. The mechanism only makes sense if one accepts the idea of knowledge as produced, and of the considerable, though imperfect, degree of volition achievable in its production. It is also necessary to make the distinction between knowledge-centered and backward firms (and industries) in order to make plausible the view that knowledge flowed predominantly in certain directions.

1. New chemical materials

When dealing with so varied and changing an industry as the chemical industry, it is not possible to cover all the new products that came on the market over some six decades. Nor is the distinction between quality changes and new products a clear one. Here we shall only consider examples of product innovations that opened up technical possibilities in the user industry, including creating it.

The uses of chemicals in textiles has already received considerable emphasis. In addition to dyes, a number of finished materials, bleaches, mordants, and the like, were used. Eventually, however, the chemical industry was to affect textiles most strongly by providing a whole class of new materials, the artificial or synthetic textiles[2]). During the period before 1914, only a few artificial textiles, mainly rayon, were developed. The chemically related field of synthetic resins, or plastic materials, also got a start before 1914. Here, too, a sizeable new processing industry was to develop, and in both cases the products contributed to new technical possibilities in user industries.

It should be noted that dyestuffs found many uses outside the textile field, notably in leather, paper printing, and wood finishing.

Metallurgy was able to broaden the spectrum of its production considerably, owing to the variety of new metals made available largely as a result of thermochemical and electrothermal developments. These techniques allowed the ores of high-melting metals to be reduced. As in the case of new dyes, where the main effect was to allow improvements in the dyeing process, the new metals, such as manganese, chromium and tungsten, were of major importance as alloying materials for ferrous and other metals. But the most common, and the most chemical, of the newer non-ferrous metals was aluminum. Although the aluminum industry has become in part separate from the chemical industry, they were closely related in the early stages, and in France still are[3]). Metallurgy also used new chemical materials for ore flotation, soldering, lubrication, and the like[4]).

The third partner closely associated with the non-ferrous metals/chemicals complex was the electrical industry. We are not concerned with the contribution of electrical energy to chemical technology, although it was considerable. But in the other direction, chemicals provided refractory materials, insulators, lubricants, and coatings, and were a major early market for current[5]). Also associated with electricity and non-ferrous metals were the industrial gases, which became significant around the turn of the century. Griesheim Elektron, a leader in electrochemicals, also pioneered in industrial gases, and in fact developed a hydrogen/oxygen welding torch in 1906[6]). But French industry was also active in this area, in particular l'Air Liquide, founded in 1902[7]).

In other lines, great new technological possibilities were opened up by seemingly small changes in chemicals, particularly by the availability of pure and standardized products. In two cases especially, enamelling and glass-making, this provided the impetus for a systematic approach to a technology that had been entirely empirical[8]). Only when it was possible to obtain a variety of chemical products of reagent quality in industrial quantities and at ordinary prices could the methods of chemical science find practical application in traditional process technology. The first step in applying science was to investigate the composition of the products, and this did not pay until there was a good prospect of controlling as well as determining it. The electrical industry also benefited from the availability of pure metals for conductors[9]).

The secondary effects of chemical innovation on primary production were generally favorable, though less uniformly so. Artificial textiles and resins competed with natural materials, synthetic dyes replaced agricultural products, and there were other substitutions. But new branches of mining grew up to provide raw materials, such as sulfur, pyrites, bauxite, phosphates, potash, and fluorspar. And even in traditional primary products, the chemical industry contributed to new vigor. The example of coal has been mentioned, but wood, iron, fibers, and food were also made more versatile and profitable with the help of chemical materials. Treated wood was a better construction material, while chemically cooked wood fibers were turned into paper, whose production grew enormously. In the Savoie, chemical processes for pulping wood allowed the paper industry to diversify away from the limited market for its traditional high-quality rag papers[10]). Chemicals were used to alloy steel, to treat natural fibers, and to preserve and process food.

2. Chemicals and the diffusion of techniques

Technical and scientific knowledge spreads between firms and industries in an economy, and between economies. There is also a flow between firms and other sources and users of knowledge, such as government and university laboratories and private inventors. Histories of technology emphasize the initial source of particular innovations (related and useful items of knowledge) but they tend to slight the conditions governing diffusion. I have argued that knowledge-centered firms will be particularly avid users of new knowledge to which they have access, since it will often complement and be complemented by their own activity. In addition, they will be sources of knowledge that eventually becomes available to others. Although their technical effort is primarily directed at solving problems of economic relevance to themselves, the knowledge gained may be applicable elsewhere. Also, technical effort does not always and only result in answers to specific problems. It may yield unexpected but valuable innovations, or even be undertaken with no closely specified object in mind. One would expect industrial research to yield comparatively applied knowledge or directly usable innovations, partly because development requires more capital than invention, and partly because technical effort by firms has an operational bias.

The foregoing *a priori* considerations are necessary because the precise role of the chemical industry in developing widely applicable methods and techniques is hard to document directly. Yet the chemical industry occupies a special place in the history of technology, if one accepts as valid the concept of knowledge-centered operation. Although chemicals were not the only branch of industrial production based on the application of science in the 19th century, they were the first *process* industry so operated. The process industries are a large and ancient group, encompassing the manufacture of glass, petroleum products, soap, cement, metals, ceramics, pulp, and many other products, as well as the treatment of water, fibers, leather, and wood, and the processing of food and other agricultural materials. They have been characterized even in pre-industrial times by relatively complex technology, but often of a highly empirical character. Process technology outside the chemical industry remained scientifically backward well into the 20th century, and still relies partially on prescientific methods[11]. In part this may have its roots in entrepreneurial inertia, but a contributing factor is the enormous chemical and physical complexity of many natural materials and of their transformation. It was easier to make useful products, using tried-and-true techniques, than to understand why the latter worked. Technical effort, such as it was, strove to maintain standards and avoid deterioration rather than seeking improvement.

Whatever the reasons, technical effort was held back in most of the process industries, and progress in the use of more exact methods relied considerably on developments elsewhere. The leadership of the chemical industry in devising techniques and equipment appropriate to process industries complemented the work of scientific laboratories and research stations. The technical problems of process technology are to a large extent independent of the particular process, and can be dealt with along functional lines. Thus, technical effort in chemicals was concerned with such problems as corrosion, process control, analysis of composition, physical testing of materials, standards of testing, and nomenclature. The methods, reagents, instruments, and data that resulted from this concern were often useful to other process industries. Specific accounts are hard to find, and the direct connection with the chemical industry even harder to trace. But there are a number of mentions in the literature of the positive effects on specific industries of adopting chemical methods, particularly in the above problem areas[12].

Medical technology and the production of drugs benefited greatly from the introduction of chemical methods, as well as from products developed directly by chemical firms[13]). The connection between chemicals and medicine is an old one. In the 19th century, phenol from coal-tar was used as an antiseptic, and the first dyestuff was a by-product of research by Perkin into the chemistry of quinine. Later, the direction of effects was reversed, with by-products of dyestuff research finding medical applications.

Although the chemical industry had a deficit in the exchange of knowledge with the scientific community, the flow was not all one way. Research everywhere was helped by new techniques, reagents, and instruments. Chemical companies carried out and sponsored pure research, and their scientists published in journals and were active in the learned and professional societies[14]). The work at BASF in thermodynamics and high pressure technology in connection with the ammonia synthesis found uses in other industries concerned with heat engineering and compressed fluids[15]).

Finally, the chemical industry kept many of the incidental benefits of its own research. The great indigo project at the BASF, which lasted from 1880 to 1897, resulted in a process for liquefying chlorine and in the development of hydrosulfite bleaches, in addition to providing the impetus for the contact process to make concentrated sulfuric acid[16]). The experience with catalysts gained from the latter was put to use in working out the ammonia synthesis some years later. Höchst also experienced 'technological fallout' from its indigo research, mainly in the direction of chlorine and electrochemicals[17]).

3. The external effects of technical effort

The process of diffusion of technical knowledge is characteristic of any growing economy, and there is no particular reason to single out the chemical industry as a leading sector because it both applied the findings of science and contributed to the corpus of scientific and technical knowledge. For one thing, its contribution is not well measured by the degree to which other industries adopted chemical methods, or used new chemicals to improve their technology, even in instances when the innovation originated in the chemical industry. As we have argued before, the adaptation and adoption of knowledge is a form of technical effort, so that rapid and vigorous imitation is only quantitatively different from innovation when they are distinguishable at all. New materials might be used like the old, despite their changed properties, or not used at all, just because they were different. And new methods could be ignored, or rejected after a hasty and skeptical trial because they would not work without some adaptation. In addition, if all that is needed for growth in relatively backward industries is available knowledge, then there is no need to have technologically leading sectors, unless there is no source of similar technology anywhere, including abroad. The problem of technological lag, of backward and progressive economies and sectors, would then have to be explained entirely in terms of scarce factors of production or of so-called non-economic causes.

At this point we introduce a central argument of this book. It relates to the fact that profit-maximizing knowledge-centered firms are led to direct technical effort at technologies other than their own. If there are industries that are backward (i.e., hampered in their growth by inadequate technical effort), they may experience sizeable gains in productivity as a result of the technical effort carried out in the knowledge-centered sector.

The simple model with which we are dealing involves a knowledge-centered industry that buys from and sells to backward ones[18]). Although the former is suitably efficient and progressive, its growth is limited by inelasticities of supply and demand and by the limited growth of backward sectors. In Chapter 3 we saw how the technically progressive firm operated within the constraints of its economic environment. Substitutes were found for costly or inelastically supplied inputs, new markets prospected and new products developed. But there is a second way. The knowledge-centered firm can change the technology of other industries, and thereby modify the supply and demand functions relevant to its own operations.

The mechanism is operative if there is enough potential for productive technical effort in the backward sectors so that the firm carrying out the effort is repaid by the shift in the demand (or supply) curve it faces. This 'payment' can represent only a part of the gain due to technical change, since the customer's new demand schedule, for example, yields him more profit than did the old. Were this not so, the backward firms would have no reason to adopt the technology. Since I have argued that backwardness, in the sense used here, involves entrepreneurial inertia, it is likely that the user or supplier industry will require a strong incentive before it will accept change, even when the necessary technical effort is provided from the outside.

It can therefore be seen why the argument relies strongly on the distinction between knowledge-centered and backward firms and industries, and on their sharply differing propensities to engage in technical effort. For technical effort to promote growth in another sector, it must offer considerable opportunities for technically successful and economically profitable investment in the production of knowledge, and yet such investment must not be forthcoming on the part of the firms directly concerned. The implied disequilibrium is strengthened by the presumption that, *ceteris paribus*, it is more costly to work on an unfamiliar technology, so that the outside, knowledge-centered firm would normally be at a disadvantage if the inside firms were not unwilling to engage in technical effort.

It is a fact that firms do try to shift the demand and supply functions conditioning their operations by means of technical effort. Leaving aside for a time the evidence from our case (and current industrial practice yields many more examples), how does the fact fit into the economic theory of production? If we assume that the coexistence of knowledge-centered and backward firms or groups of firms is an equilibrium phenomenon, then true external economies are involved. The production function of one firm (the backward one) depends on the activity of another firm, which modifies it by means of technical effort. Note that the external economy is a technological one, since it affects the relationship between the physical inputs and output of the backward firm. If we prefer to think of backwardness, i.e., the failure to engage in the technically optimal amount of technical effort, as the result of non-maximizing behavior, then the effect of outside technical effort is to allow backward firms to operate as if they were economically rational. I prefer to think of this phenomenon as a true case of external economies, in part because it is always uncomfortable to assume that firms fail to maximize over an extended period of time, and in part because I have argued that firms and industries are likely to be backward or knowledge-centered, rather than being distributed unimodally.*

---

* On the face of it, the knowledge-centered firm is enjoying *pecuniary* external economies as it observes favorable shifts in the market schedules that condition its profits. But the shifts are planned results of purposive activity by the firm, and are therefore not real externalities.

It goes without saying that the idea of informational costs being associated with buying and selling is not a new one. Like transport costs in the theory of international trade, they are often mentioned and as often neglected. The main exception is advertising, where selling costs are intended to provide information and sometimes to change tastes, but there is doubt about the reliability of the former and the propriety of the latter. In the present case, however, the scope and function of selling (or buying) effort are far larger. The information must be produced as well as disseminated, and it does more than allow the receiver to maximize within existing technology.

4. The chemical industry and transmitted knowledge

Chemical firms were led to investigate unfamiliar technologies for a variety of reasons, some involving difficulties in existing or planned operations, and some the search for new opportunities or better market conditions. Often the technology still lay within the chemical industry, although it was new to the firm. Here we are not concerned with diversification as such, i.e., the decision to undertake a new line of production, but with technical effort in the technology of products the firm would normally buy from others.

We have already noted the decision of the German dyestuff houses to make their own inorganic chemicals in the face of cartels in soda and sulfuric acid. A more characteristic case is that of the corrosive chemicals which became important at the end of the 19th century: fuming sulfuric acid, nitric acid, chlorine, and caustic soda. Until large-scale organic syntheses created a massive demand, these difficult materials had been made in small quantities and at high cost by archaic methods, and reserved for special uses such as precious-metal refining and laboratory work. When truly industrial quantities were required, the appropriate technologies were developed. The BASF sponsored Winkler's work on the contact process for concentrated sulfuric acid, while both the BASF and Höchst were active in the development of the electrolytic and nitrogen-fixing processes on which the supply of the other substances depended.

In other cases, the technical effort was aimed at the technology of suppliers to the chemical industry. As early as 1838–40, French and English manufacturers of sulfuric acid developed a substitute for precarious supplies of Sicilian sulfur by roasting sulfur ores of metals, i.e.

pyrites. Later, the Solvay company was a leader in the development of by-product recovery coking ovens, and Brunck, of the BASF, contributed to the process by his method of scrubbing benzol (the lightest liquid fraction of coal distillate) from coke-oven gas, patented in 1887[19]).

Our previous discussion of the coal-tar question indicated that Germany derived considerable profit from these developments. Three reasons for her lead in devising and adopting the new technique may be adduced. The demand of the chemical industry is one, but this operated in Britain too, since the British had previously supplied much of the continental demand for tar. Stagnation in British agriculture presumably limited the market for ammonium sulfate, a by-product of tar production which was heavily used in Germany as a fertilizer. Another reason is the technical effort of the chemical industry itself, as indicated by the work of Solvay and the BASF. But it is clear that there was also a commitment to technical effort on the part of coal and metallurgical concerns in Germany, since the chemical industry was only partially responsible for by-product coking. In Britain, on the other hand, where the stimulus of a strong dyestuff industry was lacking, the same unwillingness to engage in technical effort was also characteristic of coal and steel men. Inquiry into the desirability of adopting the new ovens consisted of short and superficial experiments which allowed 'prejudices [to be] confirmed'[20]). Manufacturers were not organized for regular investigation, and no single innovation was likely to justify or force the switch to knowledge-centered operation of the firm.

With reference to the specific mechanism which concerns us here, the failure of the coal and steel firms in Britain could not be compensated by the technical effort of other, more knowledge-centered firms with an interest in the technology, since there were none in Britain. I would stress the fact that the British lag was due to the absence of *domestic* technical effort, since the technical knowledge was easily available on the continent, and even the equipment could be purchased. But the technical effort involved in deciding that change would in fact be profitable could, apparently, only be done at home. As we shall see in the case of customers of the chemical industry, however, it probably need not have been done by the coke makers themselves. A chemical industry interested in more and cheaper tar and intermediates might have turned the trick, undertaking the work of proving the superiority of the new method, and offering assistance with the technical problems involved in change.

When Bosch of the BASF was working out the technique of synthesizing ammonia, one problem involved the metal reactors[21]). At the high temperatures and pressures of the reaction, all known steels were porous to hydrogen. Bosch and his co-workers investigated the possibilities of making suitable alloys, and thus provided a considerable stimulus to this young field. The line of chrome-nickel alloys which were finally developed with the Krupp works for the process were among the first important stainless steels, while valuable experience was gained in forming high-pressure vessels and in working alloys[22]). There is no doubt that the bulk of the technical effort was carried out by the BASF, and the question of steel for reactors is only one of many technical areas in which the firm had to innovate during the ammonia project.

Despite these significant examples, and I believe that their number reflects limitations of information rather than the actual number of relevant cases, there was comparatively little scope for the chemical industry to exert any considerable influence on the technology of producing its inputs. These were relatively few in number, and barring unprocessed raw materials required little special technology. The main exception involved equipment for chemical processing, a branch of industry which only began its development before World War I. The more knowledge-centered firms preferred or were forced to make for themselves any complex pieces. Although they undoubtedly were responsible for many innovations, and gathered information useful to the making of process equipment in general, I have found little literature on the early development of process equipment technology.

The chemical industry devoted far more technical effort to the technology of its customers. They were a much larger group of firms in many industries, and included substantial and relatively backward sectors. Foremost among them were textiles and agriculture, but most process industries used chemical products as well. We shall look at the textile industry's use of chemical technical effort, at the work in fertilizer technology, and at the way in which small firms in chemical specialties benefited from the knowledge-centered character of their suppliers.

Perhaps the reader will feel that the evidence is too sparse to justify fully the stress placed on technical effort as a way of changing other firms' production functions. I will grant that there is an element of hindsight involved in suggesting that such transmitted technical progress can be a substantial force promoting growth. The instruments and policies by which chemical firms extended the range of their technical effort in the 19th century have become more common and more highly elaborated in recent decades. Yet in a sense their very universality may now weaken the strategic force for growth they represent. If technical effort is widespread in an economy, then most firms are simultaneously generating and absorbing the external economies associated with technical effort in other technologies. Their own productivity gains from others' technical effort, while the knowledge they produce improves technology elsewhere. Only in the context of substantial backwardness is there an important asymmetry, so that it then becomes meaningful to speak of growth-promoting industries. I shall even suggest that early knowledge-centered firms contribute to the spread of this mode of operation, and are thus doubly important in the early stages of growth.

The technology of dyestuffs, dyeing, and related operations in textile finishing was highly developed before the introduction of synthetic dyes. Among the technical as well as economic leaders were firms in Lyons and Mulhouse, and it is no coincidence that early French research on aniline colors was concentrated in the dyeworks of these cities. Soon, however, the magnitude of the scientific effort involved and the departure of many early workers from France made dye manufacturers independent of users. Cooperation in technical effort was still necessary for the development of new materials, so that the chemical firms began to operate small dye shops to test their own and their competitors' products. In these facilities they combined the systematic learning of the graduate with the intuition and experience of the colorist. Basle, in particular, relied on the training and skills of men from Mulhouse, and still employs colorists from that city. The center of gravity of technical effort soon shifted clearly to the chemical industry when the activity of the experimental dye shops expanded far beyond mere testing and quality control.

An outstanding and well-documented case of pre-1914 technical effort for textiles is that of the BASF, although the other German and Swiss firms were similarly active[23]). A major aspect of the knowledge-centered character of dyestuffs producers was the realization that sales were a technical as well as a commercial matter. In the early years of the BASF, sales were handled by an autonomous, though affiliated, commercial organization, Gustav Siegle of Stuttgart. Once this activity was transferred to Ludwigshafen, a separate technical facility was assigned to the task of supporting the sales effort. In 1891, the dye shop was separated from the control laboratory, and henceforth served the needs of the research and sales functions. By 1914, the technical dye shop employed over 100 professional people. While part of its activity was in support of research, and another part concerned with non-textile applications, the sale of textile chemicals clearly involved substantial technical effort.

The company employed technically trained salesmen, and backed them up with a technical service group, first only in Ludwigshafen, later also in field sales agencies. For problems requiring more work, there was the application research group proper, which pursued its own projects in addition to supporting the sales staff[24]). It should be noted that technically trained salesmen were useful in many ways. They suggested new uses for the company's products, helped customers with technical problems, and defined problems too involved for an immediate answer, so that the laboratory could attack them more easily. But they also acted as valuable sources of information on new technical developments for the parent company, since their selling approach gave them access to the plant as well as the offices of clients.

Two functions of the sales technical organization, in addition to application research and technical service, were training and sales promotion. Of course, the salesmen and technical specialists had to be trained, since even academic or trade-school education was insufficient background for the problem-oriented work involved. But the employees of client firms were trained as well. To some extent this implanted, or was intended to implant, a favorable bias toward BASF products, but in view of the rapid changes in technology, training was necessary to make clients able as well as eager to use new materials. More was involved than the building of good will.

In promotional material as in training, the sales effort had a significant technical dimension. A BASF catalogue can serve to illustrate this[25]). It is first of all a well-produced book of 517 pages, including textile samples, and must have been costly to print and bind. But its contents also show the result of considerable expenditure, since the catalogue contains a wealth of information in addition to describing the dyestuffs themselves. It is virtually a handbook of the dyer's trade, showing processes and equipment, and including details on auxiliary chemicals, safety precautions, printing techniques, and precise formulations for dyeing various fibers. While I have no direct measure of the catalogue's relevance or usefulness to dyers, it is unlikely that so much information, which had to be valid even if not original, would have been assembled merely for show.

The dyestuff manufacturers could engage in technical effort for their customers because they were large and already committed to substantial investment in the production of knowledge. They were almost forced to compensate for the backwardness of others, since their products had insufficient markets in the absence of technical change in the processes using them. When the client (or supplier) was less backward, as for example the steel makers referred to above, and, presumably also some users of heavy chemicals such as glass and paper makers, technical effort was cooperative, or divided according to areas of competence.

Chemicals became increasingly important to agriculture in the 19th century, chiefly as fertilizers and pesticides. Yet their use was hindered by the backwardness of much of the agricultural sector. Not only was there little technical effort within agriculture, but backwardness also made it difficult to sell products developed outside[26]). Technical effort was required in order to develop the techniques for using the chemicals, to inform and convince agriculturists, and to prevent problems that arose from leading to sharp negative demonstration effects. In France, little of this appears to have been done. The leading superphosphate producer, St. Gobain, has left no record of early technical effort in fertilizers, although this may in part reflect only the traditional silence of French firms as to their affairs. I have seen a few French brochures concerning the use of fertilizers, but they are polemical in nature, replacing experiment and demonstration with heated argument.

The Stassfurt potash syndicate, on the other hand, employed a large technical sales staff, including 14 graduate chemists and 40 to 50 agronomists (in 1907)[27]). They published literature in many languages, and their brochures stressed practical demonstrations. At the very end of the prewar period the BASF organized its agricultural research as a consequence of its entry into the nitrogen fertilizer field, but the effects were felt only in the war and postwar years[28]).

A number of problems made large-scale technical effort important. The relation between fertilizer use and crop yield involves many interdependent variables, and the solution must often be a series of recipes giving the appropriate fertilizer mix and method of application for given crops and local conditions[29]). It is important to have the right fertilizer, since inappropriate dosage is worse than useless and can result in the loss of a crop. Even if no harm is done, the absence of one necessary element means that adding more of other constituents does no good. This was shown after World War I when German agricultural yields went down despite greater use of potash and nitrates, owing to insufficient amounts of phosphates and lime[30]). And the need for a variety of research establishments to meet local conditions of soil and climate is strengthened by their role as demonstration farms.

German agriculture progressed faster during the late 19th century than did French or British, and this is reflected, particularly for the case of France, in the figures for fertilizer use cited above. The question remains as to the importance of technical effort by producers in explaining the difference. There were other relevant differences between the countries, including the vastly greater scope of technical effort in Germany on the part of government experiment stations. Yet it is striking to note the correlation between agricultural progress, fertilizer use, and progress in coking. The connection is ammonium sulfate, a major source of nitrogen, and a product of by-product coking. Nor was the contribution of fertilizers merely to increase yields with given agricultural methods. Maximum productivity could only be achieved with concurrent changes in soil preparation, so that mechanization was stimulated[31]).

The specialties sector presents in even more accentuated form the picture of many small firms relying on relatively few large chemical suppliers both for products and for certain kinds of knowledge.* Unfortunately, the documentary record of this branch of industry is almost completely blank for the pre-1914 period[32]). I am forced to rely on extrapolation from more recent periods, indeed from current practice. The range of products, however, is sufficient evidence that the branch is neither negligible in size, nor particularly recent. It includes inks, paints, varnishes, cleaning compounds, lubricants, adhesives, and other products. While many are con-

---

* Although the name chemical specialties is now commonly used to designate the types of business under discussion, I have used that term to designate more clearly chemical companies, and will refer here to specialties or parachemical firms.

sumption goods, there are also many with industrial uses, and their contribution to technology is appreciable.

Parachemical firms typically engage in a certain amount of empirical technical effort, and may even get their start when an inventor seeks to market some preparation he has devised. But their main activities are compounding, packaging, and marketing. They rely on suppliers, in particular chemical firms, for most inputs requiring complex processing. And as in the cases considered above, they buy not only goods but knowledge, in the form of technical service and of formulations, instructions, and suggested uses. In this way, a labor-intensive and small-scale industrial branch can experience technical change of a kind which, I have argued, normally requires technical effort and its concomitants of scale and capital.

Technical effort for customers was performed by chemical firms in other cases than those discussed above. A few examples for which I have found some evidence will serve to round out the discussion. Dyestuffs found many non-textile applications. The BASF archives contain literature describing their use with soap, food, buttons, wax, wood, and other materials[33]). The same firm was also concerned with bleaching and with leather tanning and dyeing. Special machinery was developed to work the chrome tanning process. There are also records of application research on the part of French firms. Kuhlmann, the founder of a major firm, did research on uses for chemicals in sugar refining, textiles, and agriculture (nitrate fertilizers), while the Coignet Company of Lyons developed formulations for the use of their phosphorus and bone glues.

5. The institutional aspects of transmitting technical progress

Although assistance by a manufacturer in the use of his product was not unknown before chemical firms began it, it had been confined to large-scale capital goods. Chemical firms that were to undertake technical effort in other technologies developed organizational forms to handle this function. One was application research, which served as part of the internal development effort in addition to providing the sales force with a laboratory and specialized knowledge. Another, and related, innovation was technical service. The technical service man is intermediate between the salesman and the laboratory, handling problems in the field which are complex enough so that they require an expert either to solve them or to formulate precise questions for the home laboratory.

As even a cursory examination of present-day trade publications will show, not only is technical service almost universally provided by sellers of materials and equipment to industry, but it is often the manufacturers' chief selling point. An advertisement for packaging film shows a roll of film topped by a hat, and is captioned: 'Film and man for the price of the film alone'[34]. The caption is of course false, in the sense that the equilibrium price of the product must include an allowance for the real resource costs of the technical effort provided. The inference is presumably that the user would have to incur much higher costs to receive the same information in other ways, such as having his own experts on the processing and testing of films.

In the modern period, and in highly developed economies, technical effort is provided for users, or even for suppliers, because specialization is efficient. Forward linkages, i.e., the provision of information to customers by sellers, predominate because most firms are more highly specialized in their sales than in their purchases. Firms use the technical effort of suppliers even when they are not backward because it is cheaper than their own for a particular purpose. But in the context of early growth or retarded development, in one industry or in a large part of the economy, technical effort from a knowledge-centered supplier or customer may be the only source of regular and purposive progress. Application research provides the opportunities, whereas technical sales and service perform the effort necessary to secure adoption of the new materials and now-optimal technology.

A striking feature of the continued growth of industrial countries would seem to be the extension of knowledge-centered operation to more and more firms and industries, and to the whole range of functions within the firm. The chemical industry was a leader on both counts, among the first to make technical effort a regular and substantial part of the production process, making direct economic use of scientific work[35]. And Duisberg's organization of the Leverkusen plant was an early example of modern management techniques[36].

How much influence did the chemical industry have on the spread of technical effort in industrialized countries? To this I can suggest no firm answer. To a large extent, technical effort is encouraged by the existence of a scientific base for the technology, and this base may originate outside the industry. A growing body of scientific knowledge about materials and processes has made effective technical effort on a reasonable scale possible, and more firms and industries have begun to use and produce exact knowledge. But the existence of knowledge-centered suppliers, customers, and potential competitors must have had some effect.

Firms dealing with knowledge-centered suppliers or customers found themselves in an environment in which standardization and precise, rational calculation were the norms. Goods were sold and bought according to specifications, and regularly tested by exact methods. Technology was made available, but in a more abstract and precise fashion, with numbers replacing the experienced intuition of master workmen. The catch, of course, was that backward firms were in some sense dependent on their suppliers, who furnished necessary knowledge along with goods. Only when the client firm undertook its own technical effort could it choose rationally among competing suppliers, and buy the optimal package of goods and knowledge. Thus, the transition to more technical effort was furthered in a number of ways, by contact with knowledge-centered firms. They provided an example of the value of technical effort, offered information that could complement, as well as replace, the client's own investment, and exercised a dominance that the client had an incentive to end.

In certain cases the knowledge-centered industry could apply more direct pressure for change. As we have seen, the chemical industry was a leading source of materials competitive with traditional industries, such as artificial textiles, plastics, and metals. It was also a leading supplier of auxiliary materials (and technical effort) to the industries affected. The combination has led, in recent years, to a rejuvenation of many backward firms and branches, natural textiles being an outstanding example. Here the chemical industry provided both the carrot and the stick, the innovations and the competition.

The dual role of the knowledge-centered industry in substituting for the technical effort of others in the short run while encouraging it over the long run, is striking when we consider the effect of the chemical industry on the supply of, and demand for, technically trained manpower in Europe. If we view the stock of human capital as a scarce resource, as students of developing economies are apt to do, the chemical industry appears to have used a good deal of it. In line with the model underlying our study, the real cost of this factor must be seen as very high, since it is heavily used in technical effort, itself an important source of growth. This is mitigated by the contribution of technical effort in chemicals to progress elsewhere, particularly if we view chemical firms as efficient in their use of trained manpower owing to scale. But a more important effect is the longer-run influence of the knowledge-centered industry on technical manpower. In a growth context, the supply of a factor is as much the result of economic activity as it is a constraint.

The chemical industry in Europe exerted some direct influence on the quantity and quality of technical and scientific education. In Germany especially, contact with the universities and polytechnic institutes (*technische Hochschulen*) was close[37]. Leaders of the chemical industry were instrumental in discussions concerning curricula, particularly with regard to making university instruction in chemistry more technical[38]. In France and Switzerland, contacts were less important. The first contribution of the Basle chemical industry to the city's university dates from 1896, while the Zurich polytechnical institute, the *ETH*, had little connection with the Swiss chemical industry[39]. French industry had little interest in scientific education, although it did support the more vocational schools of industrial chemistry in such places as Lyons and Lille[40].

Far more important than this, however, was the encouragement given to technical training by the demand for graduates, and by the important role technically trained men were given in chemical firms, particularly in Germany. With respect to the demand for chemically trained men in the economy as a whole, the chemical industry economized on the scarce resource in the short run by using it efficiently in a few firms. But over time, the encouragement given to technical effort elsewhere has greatly increased the demand for technical men. Textile firms, for example, have in recent times hired chemists in order to free themselves from dependence on chemical suppliers[41]. Finally, technical effort concerned with heretofore empirical technology, whether carried out within the industry in question or outside, has stimulated inquiry into the underlying scientific principles. Such basic research has in turn facilitated the spread of technical effort in the backward industry.

The key to evaluating the role of the chemical industry in the growth of western European economies has proved to be its contribution to technical progress. This in turn depended on technical effort, the same factor that went furthest toward explaining comparative growth within the industry. Given that progress required a greater allocation of resources to the production of knowledge than was common in partly industrialized economies, an industry which did engage heavily in technical effort could play a constructive role. It generated products and techniques which improved on technology in other sectors; either purposively or because of technological similarities, and helped implement, as well as create, the new possibilities. The chemical industry also imposed pressure on backward sectors to reallocate resources as traditional activities were displaced as a result of, and by, chemical innovations. .

The synergistic effect of the chemical industry was not severely limited by its modest size in relation to the industrial sector as a whole. Indeed, the requirements of the industry for trained manpower and for entrepreneurial commitment to knowledge-centered operation meant that its influence might have been limited if leverage had been a critical problem. Inelastic supplies of the necessary factors might have limited its own growth and reduced its knowledge-centered character.

Notes

1. See above, p. 111; also C. Singer *et al.*, eds., *A History of Technology*, v, (1958), p. 588. The change in printing technique was similar to that effected in paper printing by the invention of the rotary press.
2. See B. Pierre, *Les textiles artificiels et synthétiques en France* (1946).
3. See C. Gignoux, *Histoire d'une enterprise française* (1955), pp. 86ff.; also: Ugine, *Réalités* (1949), pp. 74 ff.
4. See: *Dix ans d'efforts scientifiques et industriels, 1914–1924* (1926), p. 241; and, for more recent developments, F. Ehrmann, *Chemie und industrielle Entwicklung in den letzten 25 Jahren* (1955), p. 5.
5. See M. Chêne, Industries savoyardes, *La Revue de Savoie*, Special Centenary Issue (1960), pp. 37–38; V. Barut, *L'industrie de l'électrochimie et de l'électrométallurgie en France* (1924), p. 124; H. Howe, *Chemistry in Industry* (1924), pp. 85–90.
6. The company is now a part of Höchst. See: *Farbwerke Höchst* (1953), p. 59.
7. See: *Le monde des affaires en France de 1830 à nos jours* (1952), p. 188.
8. For enamelling, see H. Hodgson, The Influence of the Chemist upon the Enamel Industry, *The Chemical World* (May 1912), p. 168; for glass, see C. Singer, p. 672; Solvay, *Soude et produits chimiques* (1889), p. 43.
9. H. Howe, pp. 85–90.

Full bibliographical data are given in the Bibliography at the end of the book.

10. M. Chêne, pp. 10–11.
11. A visit to a perfume maker or a brewery makes this clear.
12. A sampling of industries mentioned includes coal, water treatment, metals, and cement (R. Pilcher and F. Butler-Jones, *What Industry Owes to Chemical Science* (1918)); glass and ceramics (A. Zart, *Die Entwicklung der chemischen Grossindustrie* (1922), pp. 40–43); steel from the 1880s on (*100 Jahre VDE* (1960), p. 37); food and leather (R. Fisch, *Les industries chimiques de la région lyonnaise* (1923), p. 7). Guaranteed reagents were introduced by Merck of Darmstadt in 1888. See: *Die chemische Fabrik E. Merck* (1952), p. 33.
13. The interconnections are discussed in L. F. Haber, p. 133; O. Witt, Die Entwicklung der deutschen chemischen Industrie im 19. Jahrhundert, *Die chemische Industrie*, no. 7 (1903), pp. 28, 106.
14. J. Beer, pp. 64–69, discusses the ties between the German dyestuff makers and university laboratories. See also A. Bürgin, p. 195.
15. Die deutsche chemische Industrie (1930), p. 34.
16. BASF (1922), pp. 20–21.
17. H. Schall, *Die chemische Industrie Deutschlands* (1959), pp. 73–75; L. F. Haber, p. 85.
18. Purchases of primary factors of production and sales to consumers are ignored.
19. L. F. Haber, p. 86.
20. See D. Burn, *An Economic History of Steelmaking* (1961), pp. 204–207. The quote is on p. 204.
21. K. Holdermann, *Carl Bosch* (1953), p. 99.
22. *Ibid.*; also *100 Jahre VDE*, pp. 44–45.
23. I am indebted to the firm history department of the BASF for unpublished information regarding the AWETA, or technical application division. See also: *BASF schreibt Geschichte* (n.d.), *passim*.
24. *Ibid.*; M. Fauque (1932), p. 122.
25. *Die Anilinfarben der BASF und ihre Anwendungen auf Wolle, Baumwolle, Seide und sonstige Textilfasern* (1900).
26. See above, pp. 10–12, 30 and the sources cited there.
27. V. Cambon, *L'Allemagne au travail* (1909), pp. 130–131.
28. K. Holdermann, pp. 128ff.
29. Chemical companies soon developed special compound fertilizers with specified chemical and physical properties. See H. Schultze, *Die Entwicklung der chemischen Industrie* (1908), p. 248.
30. P. Frenz, *Chemische Industrie und Landwirtschaft* (1929), pp. 82–91.
31. P. De Rousiers, *Les grandes industries modernes*, v, (1924–1928), p. 82; Die Entwicklung der preussischen Landschaft, 1888–1913, *Verhandlungen des königlichen Landes-Oekonomie-Kollegiums*, xii, 3 (1913), p. 72.
32. M. Laferrère, *Lyon* (1955), p. xi, mentions the parachemical branch as an important customer of modern chemical firms in the city.
33. *Cent ans d'industrie chimique: Les Etablissements Kuhlmann, 1825–1925* (1926), pp. 4–5; J. Coignet, *Histoire de la Maison Coignet, 1818–1900* (1900).

34. *Modern Packaging*, 36, *8* (April 1963), p. 5.
35. Flechtner, pp. 101–102, says that the chemical industry followed close on Edison, who first organized the process of invention. See also A. Bürgin, *Geigy*, pp. 101–103.
36. H. J. Flechtner, pp. 142–143.
37. See A. Haller, *L'industrie chimique* (1895), p. 31; Haller, *Les industries chimiques et pharmaceutiques: Exposition de Paris 1900*, I, (1903), p. xxix; H. Schultze, *Die Entwicklung der chemischen Industrie in Deutschland seit dem Jahre 1875* (1908), p. 12.
38. J. Beer, *The Emergence of the German Dye Industry*, p. 112.
39. A. Bürgin, *Geigy*, p. 195; CIBA, *Origines et aspects de l'industrie chimique bâloise* (1959), pp. 130–131.
40. The school of industrial chemistry in Lyons, founded in 1883, received a subsidy from the Chamber of Commerce of that city. See Syndicat Commercial et Industriel de Lyon, *Travaux de la Chambre Syndicale, 1873–1893* (1894), p. 134; also M. Laferrère, pp. 493–494.
41. The point was made in conversation by Dr. Karl Menzi of CIBA (Basle).

7

Conclusion

From the middle of the 19th century until World War I, the development of the chemical industry in France, Germany, and Switzerland mirrored fairly closely the pattern of growth in the three countries: spectacular jumps in Germany, with a shift from lag to lead in technology that impressed contemporaries quite as much as did the quantitative record; slower and less uniform growth in France, where the economy was highly sensitive to the costs associated with change; and, steady, if quiet progress in Switzerland, where human skills and environmental stability more than compensated for limitations of scale and resources. Success was closely associated with the willingness of entrepreneurs to devote resources to the production of knowledge, and it was in those branches of the industry most dependent on technical effort that the lead of Germany and Switzerland was greatest. Differences in the market environment facing the national industries mattered little, if at all, as is seen by the strong export orientation of the flourishing dyestuff manufacturers. Other external factors, in particular public policy and the educational system, conditioned technical effort and so were more relevant to successful development.

Despite its small size, the chemical industry had appreciable effects on the process of economic growth, chiefly in encouraging greater productivity and efficient reallocation. The rapid gains in productivity enjoyed by chemical firms were reflected in a number of ways. One part allowed fast growth and continued progress, owing to heavy reinvestment of high earnings. Another portion was reflected in lower prices, and an important part emerged in the form of more productive chemicals, as opposed to merely cheaper ones. Finally, a portion of the expenditure for technical effort was devoted to improving other technologies and inducing firms in other industries to adopt new products and the improved methods they made possible. The chemical industry was an elastic supplier of useful products, a partial substitute for inadequate technical effort elsewhere, and an example of the value of knowledge-centered production.

The action of the chemical industry in promoting reallocation was not entirely benign. An important mechanism was competitive pressure, which forced resources out of traditional lines of production. In the French economy, which had a rather good pre-industrial resource position and found reallocation consistently painful, chemical progress often led to difficulties. It proved easy, at least in the case of new textile technology, to prevent domestic producers from undermining the old comparative advantage, but foreign competitors were another matter. The alternative to flexible allocation and rapid adoption of new techniques was slow growth, and forces encouraging reallocation, or making available new technology, emphasized the cost of standing still. The absence of a complete commitment to industrialization in France was reflected, in chemicals as elsewhere, in a distaste for the discipline and opportunities associated with foreign trade.

Chemicals, and technical advances in chemicals even more so, were saving of natural resources. The industry was thus especially suited to Switzerland, which had few resources, and to Germany, where the supply of natural resources was considered a potential bottleneck. In France, as we have seen, there was resistance to this effect of chemical progress, since greater effective abundance of raw materials meant lower returns to the owners of existing supplies. The United States, where chemicals developed tardily, had few resource problems. But Great Britain poses an interesting problem, particularly in view of H. J. Habakkuk's investigation of 19th-century technical change in the British economy[1]).

Until the 1860s, the British chemical industry progressed rapidly. There were few changes in the basic technology, and Britain enjoyed a favorable position in resources, labor, and capital. As Habakkuk suggests, conditions were favorable for capital widening, and for the incidental (but not necessarily minor) technical improvements that accompanied new investment[2]). In the latter part of the century, resources, and perhaps also labor, became scarce relative to capital. There should have been a shift to capital-using and resource-saving investment and innovation. The character of progress through technical effort possible in chemicals made the industry a potential leading sector, yet Britain clearly lagged in this area.

Habakkuk suggests that there is an inherent bias in innovation against resource-saving change[3]). This is not borne out by the history of the chemical industry. But the shift to a different kind of technical progress than had been achieved with rapid investment under easy factor market conditions demanded a substantial change in the organization of chemical production. This change I have called the shift to knowledge-centered operation, and in Britain it was not forthcoming. Entrepreneurs had incentives to economize on the use of natural resources, but were unwilling or unable to invest in the necessary technical effort, particularly when this involved the systematic application of science, as it did in chemicals. Our analysis of growth in the chemical industry on the continent also suggests that Habakkuk's emphasis on the patent system is somewhat misplaced[4]). Entrepreneurial attitudes to technical effort, and the demand of firms for technical manpower in conjuction with the educational system that supplied it, appear to have more explanatory power in the case of Britain too.

The general conclusion regarding the comparative performance of France and the other two countries (Britain being again relegated to one side) is subject to qualification on account of two biases in the evidence. One is the far greater amount of information available concerning the extent and organization of technical effort in German and Swiss firms. As I have pointed out previously, French firms did employ technical personnel and carry out experimental work. Just how extensive this effort was, the published record fails to show, and the existing firms have not permitted me to examine their archives, even for so remote a period. On the one hand, managers appear to have played down the extent of technical effort, since stockholders considered this an unjustified drain on cash flow, and therefore on dividends[5]). On the other hand, it remains true that technical effort in French chemical firms was largely a response to competitive pressure, rather than an autonomous search for innovations. As a result, it lacked the continuity and scale conducive to maximum productivity.

The other bias stems from the fact that much of the best work done in France before 1914 came from outside the established firms in the industry, and involved technologies whose applications matured late in the period, or during and after Word War I. Moreover, the contemporary literature regarding the chemical industry used the organic industry as a frame of reference, particularly in works written under the influence of wartime shortages in chemicals with uses in munitions.

1. Observations on French economic growth

The relatively slow growth and incomplete modernization of France during the 19th century, and well into the 20th, has been a lively subject of debate for economic historians, and one of particular interest to me. For this reason, I would like to offer a few comments from this study that bear on the general problem.

Those authors who have argued that France was held back chiefly by poor natural resources and difficult transport conditions find scant comfort from the history of the chemical industry. Although progress in chemicals could, and elsewhere did, help to counteract deficiencies in raw material supplies, in France there was neither sufficient technical effort in chemicals nor the willingness to reallocate resources so as to ease the raw material position. And the supposed lack of natural resources does not explain the failure of France to develop her chemical industry to the full.

The history of the chemical industry casts more light on the role of government and that of entrepreneurs in retarding growth, and in both instances inadequate technical effort appears to have been the major difficulty. Government was unwilling to change public policy in response to the requirements of a more complex and technological society, which exacerbated the constraints imposed by a precarious social balance. Industrialists suffered from their insistence on retaining control and from their distaste for moderate and sustained risk-taking. They were technically competent, and often more, but this only strengthened their reluctance to engage substantial external resources in technical effort.

The evidence regarding the role of capital and education is somewhat mixed. There was inadequate investment in both tangible and human capital, but the fault may lie with the supply of resources, with the intermediates (banks and schools, respectively), or with the demand of the industrial sector for venture capital and technically trained manpower. Judging from the evidence of the chemical industry, the institutional conditions for providing the two kinds of capital were less than ideal, but a major factor was undoubtedly the reluctance of firms to seek capital outside or to expend it on technical effort.

The general impression that emerges regarding the conditions of economic expansion in France is that the costs associated with change were weighted heavily both in individual decision-making by firms, and in political and collective processes. Since growth without reallocation was not possible, there was retardation, and change-accelerating innovations, such as knowledge-centered production, were particularly resisted.

Although the broad picture remained unchanged until 1914, and indeed until World War II, there is clear evidence of increased technical and economic dynamism after 1890–95. Although the French lag in organic chemicals was not affected by this, the new industries of light metals, electrochemistry, artificial fibers, and industrial gases were well represented in France, as were, of course, the burgeoning automobile and aircraft branches. What the long-run effects might have been in the absence of the World War is a matter for speculation. War accelerated the pace of technical change, but was so costly in terms of manpower that the interwar period was negatively affected on balance.

2. A summary of the economic argument

Our study of the chemical industry, both as object and subject in the process of economic growth has relied on the concept of technical effort, systematic and resource-using activity for the production of economically relevant knowledge. I would like to suggest briefly wherein this concept may make a contribution to the theory of production. The fundamental idea, that technical progress is not manna, is hardly a new one, although its implications have received surprisingly little emphasis in the literature, given the importance accorded increased productivity in accounting for economic growth.

Technical effort is primarily the production of knowledge by firms, and in connection with the production and sale of goods. The reason for concentrating on joint production of knowledge and goods is to sharpen the distinction between technical effort and research, which is only one of its components. I have argued that the role of produced knowledge in economic efficiency extends beyond the provision of new recipes or blueprints for production. It includes the process of exploration of needs and possible technical approaches to meeting them, the adaptation of techniques to particular conditions, the decision to change techniques or products, and the technical aspects of selling effort. Although research and, to a lesser extent, development can often be performed outside the firm, say by a foreign firm or government research agency, the other aspects are difficult to separate from the firm's operations. They would seem to require the market incentive and close association with production. When a firm is unwilling or unable to engage in technical effort, it seems destined to remain backward unless another firm has the incentive to substitute its own technical effort for that of the backward firm.

While it is true that technical effort includes empirical investigation, the emphasis in the study of the chemical industry has been on the application of science. I would suggest that there are fairly strict limits to the feasible scope of technical effort in a firm in the absence of a good scientific base and of scientific methods. Handling great quantities of imperfectly specifiable information poses problems, while exact science permits a higher degree of direction and predictability in the process of producing knowledge. In turn, technical effort is unlikely to be successful unless carried out on a reasonable scale. The result is that the existence of a backlog of scientific knowledge concerning the technology is a strong stimulus to knowledge-centered operation. In the long run, however, the direction of basic scientific research is responsive to economic forces, so that technical effort encourages (and includes) fundamental work.

It has, of course, been recognized that technical progress involves more than invention. Economists have distinguished development and innovation as forms of technical progress not covered by the usual notion of the creative spark culminating in a patent. What has been somewhat slighted, I feel, is the extent to which technical change is the result of economic decisions, and, conversely, the degree to which economic maximization is a technical phenomenon. The concept of technical effort rectifies this by making the investment of resources in knowledge production an economic decision, and by requiring at least some of this investment for efficiency even within 'given' technology. On the further assumption that there are economies of scale in technical effort, particularly in the sense that resources can be shifted and shared between different tasks, it follows that firms which innovate will also be efficient as regards their reaction to changes in the market environment.

Economists have also been concerned with the rate at which new techniques are adopted, either in terms of the interval between invention and adoption, or of the lag between first and general use. While demand, factor prices, and the rate of gross investment are all relevant to diffusion, the extent of technical effort also plays a part. This is true because knowledge available from outside is usually not entirely suited to a particular firm, and because the decision to change is itself an information-using activity. For this reason, the apparent rate of return to technical effort in a firm may be very high, including the appropriation of knowledge produced elsewhere. The knowledge component of imitation also accounts at least in part for the paradox of persistent backwardness despite a backlog of seemingly relevant technical knowledge elsewhere.

The idea that technical effort is an activity with more predictability than is often thought also casts doubt on the currently fashionable notion of technological fallout. To be sure, expenditure in one direction will probably yield some return in the form of knowledge usable elsewhere. But this will probably be much less than the same resources could have produced if directed specifically at the incidental benefactor's problems. If, for institutional reasons, the resources can only be used in a restricted way, the incidental benefits are indeed worthwhile, but one should resist the temptation to justify military research, for example, largely on the grounds of potential non-military applications for its findings. We have seen the usefulness of technical effort performed outside the firms that made use of the knowledge gained, but this was purposive rather than incidental.

Finally, the idea that technical progress may originate in places other than those showing greater efficiency as a result, suggests that measures of productivity growth by sectors may be misleading. Measured gains in productivity will tend to understate the spread in progressiveness between knowledge-centered industries which generate progress elsewhere, and backward ones which benefit from the knowledge produced by others. The carry-over may come from goods which permit greater efficiency in their use, for instance, or be in the form of actual technical effort provided along with goods. Such externalities are certainly not easy to capture statistically.

3. The implications of the argument for purposive economic development

In the context of 19th-century Europe we have considered the role of a knowledge-centered industry in a market framework. We have concluded that inadequate development of the knowledge-centered industry retarded growth, given the existence of backward sectors which could benefit from its technical effort. More generally, knowledge-centered production creates external economies in the form of technical progress for backward industries. Moreover, technical effort can apparently not be fully replaced by external (e.g. government-sponsored) research, or by taking over a backlog of more advanced technology (e.g. from more advanced countries).

Looking now at the question of purposive development in partly industrialized societies, usually called the development problem, the implications of our discussion of technical effort can be embodied in a strategy of industrial development. Scarce resources of trained manpower and entrepreneurship are concentrated on a small number of foci of technical progress. Such knowledge-centered firms use factor proportions generally inappropriate to an underdeveloped economy, and thus operate at high cost and require subsidization. However, the firms produce not only goods but knowledge, of value to their own future productivity as well as to the rest of the economy.

Such a strategy is a form of unbalanced growth. More relevantly, it bears a superficial resemblance to the policy prescriptions of those who favor industrialization despite the structure of comparative costs, and who recommend the use of capital-intensive methods. But it should be noted that the common features – high costs, modern methods of production (as judged by factor proportions), and the need for subsidy – are only *necessary* conditions for the suggested strategy of development through concentrated technical effort. It is perfectly possible to incur all the costs implied in such a violation of static efficiency criteria with no benefits in the form of knowledge usable in less favored parts of the economy. Over time, the aim is to have the knowledge-centered firms become competitive, say in the face of potential imports, owing to the specialized stock of knowledge they accumulate, and also to have other sectors begin complementing the technical effort they receive with their own production of knowledge.

The choice of knowledge-centered foci of development should take into account the type of technology and the opportunities for linkage effects of the kind that lead to transmitted technical progress. We have seen that production involving the application of science is likely to be a good choice, while linkage effects will be maximized for industries dealing with large and backward sectors either as customers or suppliers. It need hardly be said in this context that the chemical industry is a likely candidate, and others include farm and textile machinery and agricultural processing industries.

Although a knowledge-centered firm or industry in an underdeveloped country would doubtless operate with high costs in view of the scarcity of many necessary resources, there would be an offset in the ease with which it could make use of external knowledge. The famous backlog of technology which is supposed to be the great legacy of the advanced countries to the developing ones can only be helpful if the knowledge is adapted and introduced by complementary technical effort. This effort is usually not effectively furnished by subsidiaries of firms from advanced countries, even if the parent company is highly knowledge-centered. The foreign branches rely on technical effort in the parent company, directed largely at problems and conditions faced in the central market. Since the marginal cost of this knowledge to the subsidiary is very low, it can compete in the local market despite the fact that its technology is inappropriate to local conditions.

Fig. 7 illustrates the factor price aspects of this. Isoquants A and B represent the cost, in simplified two-factor terms, of producing Q units of a product for a foreign subsidiary and a local knowledge-centered firm, respectively. Isoquant A, pertaining to the foreign firm, is defined only in

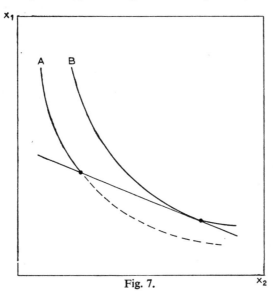

Fig. 7.

the capital-intensive range, and has no point of tangency with the local factor price line. The subsidiary nevertheless competes with the knowledge-centered indigenous firm because its isoquant is considerably closer to the origin in the range where both are defined. If the market situation is that shown in the figure, there is good reason to help the local firm, since it is also producing external economies in the form of knowledge helpful to the rest of the economy.

A knowledge-centered firm facing a backward market can, but need not, change the demand from that market by means of technical effort. If the market is small, the firm may well choose to sell limited quantities at low prices, made possible by the low *marginal* cost associated with knowledge-centered production[6]). Alternatively, the firm may invest in the production of additional knowledge for use by others in an effort to expand the market. There may be little difference in private profitability between the two approaches, but the second involves external economies benefiting other portions of the economy. It is not necessarily true that a foreign-owned firm will choose the first approach and a domestic one the second, but it would be a suitable objective of public policy to encourage locally knowledge-centered operation, and this may only be possible with an indigenous firm.

Finally, our emphasis on technical effort and the technical aspects of adjustment to market changes may shed light on the familiar debate concerning the terms of trade facing underdeveloped countries. Advanced countries, in which technical effort is substantial, can react in at least two ways to exogenous price changes in many internationally traded commodities. Because they are able to reallocate resources more effectively, they can shift from exporting to importing when a particular good falls in price, and vice versa for a price rise. In addition, they can direct technical effort at economizing on the use of, or substituting for, a product experiencing a substantial price rise. In the latter case, the result may be a fall in the long-run 'normal' price of the commodity as well as a reversal of the short-term increase. The products of less developed countries may thus suffer from the fact that their prices are unstable, even when the *average* price over time is not high enough to call forth much technical effort aimed at finding substitutes. And the instability is largely caused by inflexibility in patterns of production and trade, in turn traceable in part to insufficient technical effort in backward economies.

Notes

1. H. J. Habakkuk, *American and British Technology in the 19th Century* (1962).
2. *Ibid.*, p. 141.
3. *Ibid.*, pp. 159–160.
4. *Ibid.*, p. 216.
5. This is my reading of the St. Gobain annual reports.
6. It was argued in Chapter 3 that technical effort represents a quasi-fixed cost of production, so that marginal cost, i.e., incremental variable cost, is lower than for a firm with the same average cost and less technical effort.

Full bibliographical data are given in the Bibliography at the end of the book.

Bibliography

Armand, L. and M. Drancourt, *Plaidoyer pour l'avenir*. Paris, Calmann-Lévy, 1961.

Association Nationale d'Expansion Economique. *Enquête sur la production française et la concurrence étrangère*. Paris, 1917.

Bäumler, E. *Ein Jahrhundert Chemie*. Düsseldorf, Econ-Verlag GmbH, 1963.

Baldy, E. *Les Banques d'Affaires en France depuis 1900*. Paris, Librairie Générale de Droit et de Jurisprudence, 1922.

Ballot, C. *L'introduction du machinisme dans l'industrie française*. Paris–Lille, 1923.

Banet-Rivet, P. L'évolution de l'industrie chimique. *Revue des Deux Mondes*. April 1903.

Bargeron, L. *Le Commerce des Engrais*. Paris, Amat, 1906.

Barut, V. *L'industrie de l'électrochimie et de l'électrométallurgie en France*. Paris, PUF, 1924.

BASF. *Badische Anilin- und Soda-Fabrik*. Ludwigshafen, 1922.

BASF. *Die Anilinfarben der BASF... und ihre Anwendung auf Wolle, Baumwolle, Seide und sonstige Textilfäsern*. Ludwigshafen, 1900.

BASF. *AWETA (Anwendungstechnische Abteilung)*, ms., Ludwigshafen.

BASF schreibt Geschichte. Ludwigshafen, n.d.

Baud, P. *L'industrie chimique en France: Etude historique et géographique*. Paris, Masson et Cie, 1932.

Baud, P. *Chimie industrielle*. 2nd ed. Paris, Masson et Cie, 1927.

Baud, P. *Les industries chimiques régionales de la France*. Paris, Doin, 1922.

Baumgartner, R. *Die wirtschaftliche Bedeutung der chemischen Industrie in Basel*, (thesis). Basle, 1923.

Baumont, M. *La grosse industrie allemande et le charbon*. Paris, Doin, 1928.

Baumont, M. *La grosse industrie allemande et le lignite*. Paris, Doin, 1928.

Beer, J. J. *The Emergence of the German Dye Industry*. Illinois Studies in the Social Sciences *44*. Urbana, The University of Illinois Press, 1959.

Besnard, H. *L'industrie du Gaz à Paris depuis ses origines*. Paris, Domat-Montchrestien, 1942.

Binz, A. *Ursprung und Entwicklung der chemischen Industrie*. Reimer, 1910.

Blanchard, R. *La grande industrie chimique dans la France du sud-est*. Grenoble, Allier, 1928.

Blondel, G. *L'essor industriel et commercial de l'Allemagne*. 3rd ed. Paris, Larose, 1900.

Bodmer, W. *Die Entwicklung der schweizerischen Textilwirtschaft im Rahmen der übrigen Industrien und Wirtschaftzweige*. Zürich, Berichthaus, 1960.

Bosshardt, A., A. Nydegger and H. Allenspach. *Die schweizerische Textilindustrie im internationalen Konkurrenzkampf.* Zürich–St. Gallen, Polygraphischer Verlag, 1959.

Bouvier, J. *Le crédit lyonnais de 1863 à 1882.* Paris, SEVPEN, 1961.

Bruckner, A., ed., *Wirtschaftsgeschichte Basel, mit besonderer Berücksichtigung der Gegenwart.* Zürich, Lorenzscherverlag, 1947.

Brunschwig, R. *Les relations entre l'industrie charbonnière et les industries de la chimie.* Paris, Centre de Documentation Chimique, 1942.

Bürgin, A. *Geschichte des Geigy-Unternehmens von 1758 bis 1939. Veröffentlichung zum 200-jährigen Bestehen des Geigy-Unternehmens.* Basel, 1958.

Caille, A. *Coup d'œil sur le développement de l'industrie chimique dans la région rouennaise.* Rouen, Cagniard, 1926.

Caillot, R. *L'usine, la terre et la cité. L'exemple de Péage du Rousillon.* Paris, Economie et Humanisme, 1958.

Cambon, V. *L'Allemagne au travail.* Paris, Roger, 1909.

Cambon, V. *La France au travail.* Paris, Roger, 1914.

Cameron, R. E. *France and the Economic Development of Europe, 1800–1914.* Princeton, 1961.

Caro, H. *Über die Entwicklung der Teerfarbenindustrie.* Berlin, Friedlander, 1893.

Cassella. *Werk Mainkur, Leopold Cassella & Co. 1820–1934,* (unpublished typescript). 1934.

Chancrin, E. *Le problème de la fertilité des sols.* Paris, Hachette, 1936.

Chaplet, A. *Les industries chimiques modernes.* Paris, Delagrave, 1912.

Charpenay, G. *Les banques régionalistes.* Paris, Nouvelle Revue Critique, 1939.

Chêne, M. Industries Savoyardes. *La Revue de Savoie* (Special Centenary Issue). Chambery, 1960.

Chenery, H. B. Comparative Advantage and Development Policy. *American Economic Review*, March 1961, pp. 18–51.

Chimie et Industrie. *La grande œuvre de la chimie.* Paris, 1929.

Choffel, J. *Saint-Gobain, du miroir à l'atome.* Paris, Plon, 1960.

Christiansen, C. *Chemische- und Farbenindustrie.* In: A. Weber, ed., *Über den Standort der Industrien.* Vol. II, Ch. 2. Tübingen, J. C. B. Mohr, 1914.

CIBA. *Origines et aspects de l'industrie chimique bâloise.* Olten–Lausanne–Freiburg/Br., Urs Graf-Verlag, 1959.

CIBA. *Rundschau. 126,* May 1956.

Cinquante ans de perfectionnement technique. Paris, Centre de Perfectionnement technique, 1952.

Cinquantenaire de la Chambre de Commerce de Meurthe et Moselle: Revue des industries du département. Nancy, Berger-Levrault, 1905.

Clozier, R. *La Gare du Nord,* (thesis). Paris, Baillière, 1940.

Cochin, D. La houille et les matières colorantes. *Revue des Deux Mondes*, February 1884.

Coignet, J. *Histoire de la Maison Coignet 1818–1900.* Lyon, Rey, 1900.

Coignet, J. *Notice historique sur l'industrie des produits chimiques à Lyon.* Lyon, Imprimerie du Salut Public, 1894.

Cordier, E., ed., *Exposition internationale urbaine de Lyon 1914. Section* XXVI. Lyon, Légendre, 1914.

Correspondencia Economica. Wirtschafts Correspondenz, no. 33–40. Special Edition. La industria química alemana y sus máquinas y aparatos. Buenos Aires, 1953.

Dastre, A. L'industrie chimique des matières colorantes artificielles. *Revue des Deux Mondes*, June 1900.

Depitre, E. *Le mouvement de concentration dans les banques allemandes*, (thesis). Paris, Rousseau, 1905.

Dernis, R. *La concentration industrielle en Allemagne*, (thesis). Paris, Dalloz, 1929.

De Rousiers, P. *Les grandes industries modernes*. 5 vols. Paris, Colin, 1924–28.

Detoeuf, A. *Propos de O. L. Barenton, Confiseur*. Paris, Editions du Tambourinaire, 1958.

Die deutsche chemische Industrie. (Ausschuss zur Untersuchung der Erzeugungs- und Absatzbedingungen der deutschen Wirtschaft, III. Unterausschuss.) Berlin, Mittler, 1930.

Die deutsche Industrie. (Festgabe – Jubilee of Wilhelm II.) Berlin, Gebr. Weiss Verlag, 1913.

Die Entwicklung der preussischen Landschaft 1888–1913. *Verhandlungen des königlichen Landes-Ökonomie-Kollegiums*, XII, 3, 1913.

Deutschland's chemische Industrie. *Chemische Industrie*, IV, 10, October 1952.

Dix ans d'efforts scientifiques et industriels, 1914–1924. Paris, Chimie et Industrie, 1926.

Duisberg, C. *Abhandlungen, Vortrage und Reden aus den Jahren 1882–1921*. Berlin-Leipzig, Chemie, 1923.

Duisberg, C. *Meine Lebenserinnerungen*. Leipzig, Reclam, 1933.

Duisburger Kupferhütte. *75 Jahre Duisburger Kupferhütte, 1876–1951*. 1951.

Dumas, M. Le progrès dans l'industrie chimique. *Cahiers de l'ISEA*, no. 123, March 1962.

Ebert, W. *Die chemische Industrie Deutschlands*. Berlin–Leipzig, Verlag Chemie, 1926.

Ehrmann, F. *Chemie und industrielle Entwicklung in den letzten 25 Jahren*. Frankfurt a.M., 1955.

Enquête parlementaire sur le régime économique. (Industries Textiles Coton). Paris, Wittersheim, 1870.

Exposition internationale des industries et du travail de Turin, 1911. (Groupe XVIII B. Produits chimiques). Paris, Comité français des expositions à l'étranger, 1912.

Exposition universelle internationale de 1889 à Paris (Rapports du Jury international – Classe45-Produits chimiques et pharmaceutiques). Paris, Imprimerie Nationale, 1891.

Farbwerke Höchst, AG. Zur Erinnerung an die 75. Wiederkehr des Gründungstages der Farbwerke vorm. Meister Lucius und Brüning. 1938.

Farbwerke Höchst, AG. *Bericht über unserem Unternehmen*. 1953.

Farbwerke Höchst, AG. *Farbwerke vorm. Meister Lucius und Brüning 1863–1913*.

Fardeau, M. La propagation du progrès technique par l'industrie aéronautique. *Cahiers de l'ISEA*, no. 123, March 1962, pp. 149–179.

Fauque, M. *L'évolution économique de la grande industrie chimique en France*. Strasbourg, Editions Universitaires, 1932.

Ferchland, P. *Die elektrochemische Industrie Deutschlands.* (Monographien über angewandte Elektrochemie, vol. xii.) Halle, Knapp, 1904.

Fisch, R. *Les industries chimiques de la région lyonnaise.* Macon, Perroux, 1923.

Fischer, E. Meister Lucius und Brüning, die Gründer der Farbwerke Höchst, AG. *Tradition* iii, *2,* May 1958.

Flechtner, H. J. *Carl Duisberg: vom Chemiker zum Wirtschaftsführer.* Düsseldorf, Econ-Verlag GmbH, 1959.

Fleurent, E. *Les grandes industries chimiques à l'exposition universelle de 1900.* Paris, Gauthier-Villars, n.d.

Fleurent, E. *Les industries chimiques en France et en Allemagne.* 2 vols. Paris, Berger-Levrault, 1915, 1916.

Fleurent, E. *Les industries chimiques et la production générale en France.* Paris, 1920.

Fohlen, C. *Une affaire de famille au xixe siècle: Mequillet–Noblot.* (Cahiers de la Fondation Nationale des Sciences Politiques no. 75). Paris, Colin, 1955.

Frenz, P. *Chemische Industrie und Landwirtschaft.* Langendeer, 1929.

le Génie Civil. *L'évolution et le développement des principales industries: 1880–1930.* Paris, 1930.

Gendarme, R. *La région du Nord: Essai d'analyse économique.* (Etudes et Mémoires of the Centre d'Etudes Economiques, no. 20.). Paris, Colin, 1954.

George, F. *La rénovation de l'industrie chimique française.* Paris, Michel, 1917.

Gignoux, C. J. *Histoire d'une entreprise française.* Paris, Hachette, 1955.

Gofferje, W. *Absatzprobleme der Teerfarben- und Pharmazeutikaindustrie,* (thesis), Nürnberg, 1958.

Gravier, J. F. *Décentralisation et progrès technique.* Paris, Flammarion, 1953.

Griesheim. *75 Jahre Chemische Fabrik Griesheim Elektron.*

Grandmougin, E. *L'enseignement de la chimie industrielle en France.* Paris, Dunod et Pinat, 1917.

Grandmougin, E. *L'essor des industries chimiques en France.* 2nd ed. Paris, Dunod, 1919.

Grandmougin, E. and P. *La réorganisation de l'industrie chimique en France.* Paris, Dunod et Pinat. 1918.

Grossman, H. *Die Bedeutung der chemischen Technik für das deutsche Wirtschaftsleben.* (Vol. viii of Monographen über chemisch-technische Fabrikationsmethoden). Halle, Knapp, 1907.

Guglielmo, R. *La grande industrie chimique en France.* (Notes et Etudes Documentaires nos. 2302, 2307, 2311). Paris, La Documentation Française, 1957.

Guglielmo, R. *L'industrie française des engrais chimiques.* (Notes et Etudes Documentaires nos. 2157, 2170). Paris, La Documentation Française, 1954, 1956.

Guillet, L. *Les industries métallurgiques à l'avant-guerre. Leur avenir.* Paris, Dunod et Pinat, 1917.

Guillet, L. and J. Durand. *L'industrie française.* Paris, Masson et Cie, 1920.

Haber, L. F. *The Chemical Industry during the Nineteenth Century.* Oxford, Clarendon, 1958.

Haller, A. *L'industrie chimique.* Paris, Baillière, 1895.

Haller, A. *Les industries chimiques et pharmaceutiques – Exposition de Paris 1900*. Paris, Gauthier-Villars, 1903.

Hesse, A. and H. Grossmann. *Englands Handelskrieg und die chemische Industrie*. (Sonderausgabe aus der Sammlung chemischer u. chemisch-technischer Vortrage, vol. xxii). Stuttgart, Enke, 1915.

Hirschman, A. O. *The Strategy of Economic Development*. New Haven, Yale University Press, 1958.

Histoire de l'industrie et du commerce en France. 4 vols. Paris, Editions d'art et d'histoire, 1926.

Histoire documentaire de l'industrie de Mulhouse et de ses environs au 19ᵉ siècle. Mulhouse, Baden, 1902.

Hodgson, H. H. The Influence of the Chemist upon the Enamel Industry. *The Chemical World*. May 1912.

Hoffmann, W. G. *The Growth of Industrial Economies*. Manchester, 1958.

Hoffmann, W. G. *Das Wachstum der deutschen Wirtschaft seit der Mitte des 19. Jahrhunderts*. Berlin, Springer-Verlag, 1965.

Holdermann, K. *Im Banne der Chemie: Carl Bosch, Leben und Werk*. Düsseldorf, Econ-Verlag GmbH, 1960.

Horn, G. *Die deutsche chemische Industrie in ihrer Entstehungsphase*, (unpublished thesis). Köln, 1960.

Howard, E. *The Cause and Extent of the Recent Industrial Progress of Germany*. Chicago, 1907.

Howe, H., ed., *Chemistry in Industry*. New York, The Chemical Foundation, 1924.

L'Industrie chimique et la Science – Opinion de quelques savants anglais. *Revue de Métallurgie*, xii, August 1915.

Industrie und Wirtschaft in den Kantonen Basel-Stadt und Basel-Land. Genf–Basel, Internationales Wirtschaftsarchiv, 1936.

Jaeger, W. *Der Standortsaufbau der Basler Industrie*. Köln, Schroeder, 1937.

Jaquet, N. *Die Entwicklung und volkswirtschaftliche Bedeutung der schweizerischen Teerfarbenindustrie*, (thesis). Basel, 1923.

Jaubert, G. F. *Encyclopédie scientifique des aides-mémoire*. Paris, Gauthier-Villars & Masson, 1899. Nos. 227B, 236B, 257B.

Jaubert, G. F. *Historique de l'industrie suisse des matières colorantes artificielles*. Genève, George & Co., 1896.

Kalle. *75 Jahre Kalle, 1863–1938*. Wiesbaden, 1938.

Keppeler, G. *Chemisches auf der Weltausstellung zu Paris im Jahre 1900*. (Sammlung Chemischer und chemisch-technischer Vortrage, vol. vi). Stuttgart, Enke, 1901.

Kindleberger, C. P. *Economic Development*. 2nd ed. New York, McGraw-Hill Book Company, 1965.

Kindleberger, C. P. *Foreign Trade and the National Economy*. New Haven, Yale University Press, 1962.

Kockerscheidt, J. W. *Über die Preisbewegung chemischer Produkte*. Jena, VEB Gustav Fischer Verlag, 1905.

Koeck, W. Die volkswirtschaftliche Funktion der Chemie. *Der Volkswirt.* Beilage zur no. 14, April 1954.

Koelner, P. *Aus der Frühzeit der chemischen Industrie Basels.* Basle, Birkhäuser Verlag, 1937.

Kopp, E. *Wiener Weltausstellung 1873.* (Schweiz–Bericht über Gruppe III, Chemische Industrie). Schaffhausen, Baader, 1874.

Koppers, *Ein halbes Jahrhundert im Dienste der Kohleveredelung.* Essen, 1951.

Kreps, T. J. On the Chemical Phase of the Industrial Revolution. In: N. E. Himes, ed., *Economics, Sociology and the Modern World: Essays in honor of T. N. Carver.* Cambridge, Harvard, 1935.

Kreps, T. J. *The Economics of the Sulfuric Acid Industry.* Stanford, 1938.

Kuhlmann. *Cent ans d'industrie chimique – Les Etablissements Kuhlmann, 1825–1925.* Paris, 1926.

Kuske, B. *Rheinische Industrie von 1815–1915.* Köln, 1916.

Labasse, C. *Les capitaux et la région.* (Cahiers de la Fondation Nationale des Sciences Politiques, no. 69). Paris, Colin, 1955.

Laferrère, M. Les industries chimiques de la région lyonnaise. *Revue de Géographie de Lyon*, XXVII, *3*, 1952, pp. 219–256.

Laferrère, M. *Lyon, Ville industrielle.* Paris, PUF, 1960.

Laferrère, M. *Saint-Fons–Pierre Bénite: Un complexe français d'industrie chimique.* Lyon, Audin.

Lagache, M. *L'économie des industries chimiques.* Paris, PUF, 1962.

Laloux, J. *Le rôle des banques locales et régionales du Nord de la France dans le développement industriel et commercial.* Paris, Giard, 1924.

Landes, D. S. Technological Change and Development in Western Europe, 1750–1914. In: M. M. Postan and H. J. Habakkuk, eds., *The Cambridge Economic History of Europe*, vol. VI. *The Industrial Revolution and After.* Cambridge, 1965, pp. 274–585.

Laur, F. *De l'accaparement.* 3 vols., 2nd ed. Paris, SAPSI, 1900–1905.

Laurent, E. *Notice sur quelques questions importantes concernant les Sociétés Anonymes industrielles.* Paris, Fournier, 1909.

Lech-Chemie, Gersthofen. *Werksgeschichte, 1902–1952.*

Lefebvre, J. *L'évolution des localisations industrielles: L'exemple des Alpes françaises.* Paris, Dalloz, 1960.

Lehmann, W. *Die Entwicklung der Standorte der schweizerischen Industrien seit dem Ende des 19. Jahrhunderts.* Zürich, Juris, 1952.

Lepsius, B. *A. W. von Hofmann.* Leipzig, Duncker & Humblot, 1905.

Levasseur, E. *Histoire des classes ouvrières et de l'industrie en France de 1789 à 1870.* 2nd ed. 2 vols. Paris, Rousseau, 1904.

Levassort, R. *L'I.G. Farben et l'économie allemande.* (Cahiers de la Fondation Nationale des Sciences Politiques, no. 20). Paris, Colin, 1951.

Lévy, M. *Histoire économique et sociale de la France depuis 1848.* Paris, Les Cours de Droit – Institut d'Etudes Politiques, 1951–1952.

Lincke, B. *Die schweizerische Maschinenindustrie und ihre Entwicklung in wirtschaftlicher Beziehung.* Frauenfeld, Harber & Co., 1911.

Löffl, V. K. *Die chemische Industrie Frankreichs.* (Sammlung chemischer und chemisch-technischer Vortrage, vol. xxiv). Stuttgart, Enke, 1917.

Lunge, G. *Coal Tar and Ammonia.* 5th ed. vol. i. London, Gurney and Jackson, 1916.

Lunge, G. *Zur Geschichte der Entstehung und Entwicklung der chemischen Industrie in der Schweiz.* Zürich, Orell Füssli, 1901.

Lyon et la région lyonnaise en 1906. 2 vols. Lyon, Rey, 1906.

Macke, W. *Ein Beitrag zur Geschichte des chemischen Apparatewesens.* Bonn, Bouvier, 1946.

Maire, G. and R. Gendarme. *Contribution à l'étude des localisations industrielles de la région du Nord.* Lille, CERES, 1956.

Mairet, P. *La crise de l'industrie cotonnière, 1901–1905, étudiée spécialement dans les Vosges.* Dijon, Jacquot & Floret, 1906.

Marczewski, J. Y a-t'-il eu un 'take-off' en France? *Cahiers de l'ISEA,* suppl. no. 111, March 1961, pp. 69–94.

Markovitch, T. J. L'industrie française de 1789 à 1964 – Sources et méthodes. *Cahiers de l'ISEA* Série AF 4, no. 163, July 1965, pp. 1–231.

Martin St. Léon, E. *Cartells et Trusts.* Paris, Lecoffre, 1903.

Matagrin, A. *L'industrie des produits chimiques et ses travailleurs.* Paris, Doin, 1925.

Matignon, J. *L'influence de la protection légale des inventeurs sur le développement de l'industrie,* (thesis). Paris, Rousseau, 1915.

Maunier, R. La distribution géographique des industries. Paris, Giard, 1908.

Menzel, M. *Über die Standortsorientierung der deutschen chemischen Industrie,* (partial printing). Hamburg, 1935.

Merck. *Die chemische Fabrik E. Merck.* Darmstadt, 1952.

Menais, G. P. *Géographie industrielle de Lyon.* 2 vols. Paris, Hachette, 1958.

Minet, A. *Die Gewinnung des Aluminiums.* Halle, Knapp, 1902.

Ministère de l'Agriculture, du Commerce et des Travaux Publics. *Enquête sur les engrais industriels.* Paris, Imprimerie Impériale, 1865.

Mittasch, A. *Geschichte der Ammoniaksynthese.* Weinheim, Verlag Chemie, 1951.

Le Monde des Affaires en France de 1830 à nos jours. Paris, SEDE, 1952.

Monypenny, J. *Stainless Iron & Steel.* London, Chapman & Hall, 1926.

Muntz, A. Les phosphates dans l'agriculture française. *Revue des Deux Mondes,* August 1874.

Oberdorffer, K., ed., *Ludwigshafener Chemiker.* 2 vols. Düsseldorf, Econ-Verlag GmbH, 1958, 1960.

L'Opinion Economique et Financière. (Edition illustrée). Paris, 1959.

Palmade, G. *Capitalisme et capitalistes français au* xixe *siècle.* Paris, Colin, 1961.

Pasdermadjian, H. *La deuxième révolution industrielle.* Paris, PUF, 1959.

Payen, A. Les industries chimiques. *Revue des Deux Mondes,* March 1864, June 1866, December 1867.

Perlick, A. *Die Luftstickstoffindustrie in ihrer volkswirtschaftlichen Bedeutung.* Leipzig, Klinkhardt, 1913.

Perlick, A. *Der derzeitige Stand der Luftstickstoffindustrie.* Heidelberg, Rossler und Herbert, 1913.

Perroux, F. *L'économie du* XXe *siècle*. Paris, PUF, 1961.

Perroux, F. La firme motrice dans une région et la région motrice. *Cahiers de l'ISEA*, Suppl. no. 111, March 1961, pp. 11–68.

Piequet, O. *Etude sur les industries du blanchiment, de la teinture, de l'impression et des apprêts des tissus de coton au debut du* XXe *siècle dans le département de la Seine-inférieure*. Rouen, Cagniard, 1907.

Pierre, B. *Les textiles artificiels et synthétiques en France*. Paris, SPIE, 1946.

Pilcher, R. B. and F. Butler-Jones. *What Industry owes to Chemical Science*. London, Constable, 1918.

Pinnow, *Werksgeschichte der Farbenfabriken, vorm. F. Bayer & Co*. Leverkusen, 1930.

Plewe, E. Die Bedeutung der Industrie von Mannheim–Ludwigshafen. *BASF Magazine* no. 4, 1955.

Pollay, K. *Die Entwicklung der Farbenfabriken Bayer im Raume Leverkusen*, (unpublished thesis). Köln, 1950.

Poire, P. *A travers l'industrie*. Paris, Hachette, 1904.

Poulin, A. *Etude critique sur la petite et la moyenne industrie en France*. Paris, Jouve, 1919.

Quelques aspects du problème des engrais. *Etudes et Conjoncture*, August 1953, pp. 871–885.

Quillère, R. L'industrie chimique en Belgique, (typescript). Paris, Faculté des Lettres.

Radau, R. Les nouvelles couleurs dérivées du goudron de houille. *Revue des Deux Mondes*, August 1874.

Rapports et travaux sur la décongestion des centres industriels. Paris, Délégation Nationale à l'équipement, 1944.

Rassow, B. *Die chemische Industrie*. (Vol. I of *Die deutsche Wirtschaft und ihre Führer*). Gotha, Flamberg, 1925.

Redlich, F. *Die volkswirtschaftliche Bedeutung der deutschen Teerfarbenindustrie*. Munich-Leipzig, Duncker & Humblot, 1914.

Reichl, A. *Chemische Industrie und Chemieaussenhandel: Ein Vergleich der Entwicklung in zwölf Ländern*, (unpublished thesis). Mainz, 1957.

Remy, P. *L'évolution de la grande industrie chimique en France*. Montpellier, Dehan, 1943.

Renelle, V. *Du rôle des laboratoires dans l'industrie des peintures et vernis*. (No. 433 of Cours-Conférences du Centre de Perfectionnement Technique). Paris, Centre de Documentation Chimique.

Reybaud, L. *L'industrie en Europe*. Paris, Levy, 1856.

Richardson, H. W. The Development of the British Dyestuffs Industry before 1939. *Scottish Journal of Political Economy*, IX, 2, 1962, pp. 110–129.

Richeux, R. *L'industrie chimique en France: Structure et production 1850–1957*, (unpublished thesis). Paris, Faculté de Droit et des Sciences Economiques, 1958.

Riebel, P. Chemische Industrie. *Handbuch der Sozialwissenschaften*, vol. II. Göttingen, 1959, pp. 492–505.

Riebel, P. *Die Kuppelproduktion: Betriebs- und Marktprobleme*. Köln–Opladen, Westdeutscher Verlag, 1955.

Rohart, F. *La doctrine des engrais chimiques*. Paris, Masson et Cie, 1869.

Rosenstein-Rodan, P. Notes on the Theory of the Big Push. In: T. Morgan *et al*, eds., *Readings in economic development*. Belmont, California, Wadsworth, 1962.

Rosier, C. *La France agricole*. Paris, Alsatia, 1943.

Rostow, W. W. *The Stages of Economic Growth*. Cambridge, 1961.

Roth, H. *Die chemische Industrie der Schweiz als Exportindustrie*, (thesis). Basle, 1954.

Rousseau, P. *Histoires des Techniques*. Paris, Fayard, 1956.

Sack, E. A. La Fuchsine est centenaire. *Revue Générale des Matières Colorantes, Teintes*. December 1958.

Saint Gobain. *Rapports du Conseil d'Administration, 1858–1913*. (ms.).

Schall, H. *Die chemische Industrie Deutschlands*. (Vol. 2 of Nürnberger wirtschafts- und sozialgeographische Arbeiten). Nürnberg, 1959.

Schmidt, A. *Die industrielle Chemie in ihrer Bedeutung im Weltbild und Erinnerungen an ihren Aufbau*. Berlin, Walter de Gruyter & Co., 1934.

Schultze, H. *Die Entwicklung der chemischen Industrie in Deutschland seit dem Jahre 1875*. Halle, Tausch und Crosse, 1908.

Schuster, C. *Badische Anilin- und Soda-Fabrik, AG: Ein Beitrag zur Geschichte der chemischen Technik*. Ludwigshafen.

Schwabe, H., ed., *Schaffendes Basel: 2000 Jahre Basler Wirtschaft*. Basel, Birkhäuser Verlag, 1957.

Schwarz, G. *Die chemische Industrie als Wachstumsindustrie*. (Herrn Dr. Felix Ehrmann zum 60. Geburtstag). Frankfurt, Verband der Chemischen Industrie, 1961.

Schwerin von Krosigk, Lutz Graf. *Die grosse Zeit der Feuers: Der Weg der deutschen Industrie*. 3 vols. Tübingen, Rainer Wunderlich Verlag Hermann Leins, 1958.

Science et Industrie. *La technique des industries chimiques*. (No. 277bis of Mécanique [hors serie]). Paris, 1938.

Science et Industrie. *Les industries chimiques*. (No. 173). 1928.

Scitovsky, T. Two Concepts of External Economies. *Journal of Political Economy*, April 1954, pp. 143–151.

Sering, M. *Die deutsche Landwirtschaft*. Berlin, Verlag Paul Parey, 1932.

Shreve, R. N. *The Chemical Process Industries*. New York, McGraw-Hill Book Company, 1945.

Singer, C., ed., *A History of Technology*. 5 vols. Oxford, Clarendon, 1957–1958.

Slosson, E. *Creative Chemistry*. New York, Century, 1919.

Solvay & Cie. *Soude et Produits Chimiques*. (Note, Exposition universelle de Paris, 1889).

Sombart, W. *Die deutsche Volkswirtschaft im neunzehnten Jahrhundert*. 5th ed. Berlin, Bond, 1910.

Souchet, J. Ugine. *Réalités*. December 1949, pp. 73–83.

Les Soudières Réunies: 1855–1955. Paris, 1955.

Suilliot, M. *Réponses au questionnaire du Conseil Supérieur du Commerce et de l'Industrie*. Paris, 1890.

Syndicat Commercial et Industriel de Lyon. *Travaux de la Chambre Syndicale, 1873–1893*. Lyon, Imprimerie du Salut Public, 1894.

Syndicat Général des Produits Chimiques. *L'industrie chimique et les droits de douanes*. Paris, 1918.

Syndicat des Mines et Usines de sels potassiques de Stassfurt (Allemagne). (Exposition Universelle). Paris, 1900.

Syndicat des industries chimiques et parties similaires de Lille et environs. *Kuhlmann et Compagnie – 200 familles*. Lille, 1937.

Taudière, E. *Le régime douanier et les industries de la chime*. (No. 441 of Cours-Conférences – Centre de perfectionnement technique). Paris, Centre de Documentation Chimique.

Taylor, F. S. *A History of Industrial Chemistry*. London, William Heinemann, 1957.

Teneur, J. *Les industries agricoles et alimentaires de la région du Nord*. (Cahier 13). Lille, CERES, 1960.

Thery, E. *L'Europe économique et financière pendant le dernier quart de siècle*. (Special no. of L'Economiste européen). Paris, 1900.

Thorpe, T. E. *Dictionary of Applied Chemistry*. 4th ed. New York, Longmans-Green, 1937.

Tilmant, J. *L'industrie des matières colorantes en France*. Rouen, Giriend, 1915.

Touchot, F. *L'économie régionale lorraine dans l'économie nationale française*. Nancy, Thomas, 1937.

Ungewitter, C. *Chemie in Deutschland*. Berlin, Junker & Dunnhaupt, 1938.

Ungewitter, C. *Monographie über die chemische Industrie*. Berlin, RDI, 1926.

Valentin, J. *La fumure des terres dans la région de l'ouest*. 1949.

Vandange, M. L'industrie chimique et les pays sous-développés. *Chimie et Industrie*, 74, 6, December 1955, pp. 1244–1246.

Varini, G. *Die schweizerische chemische Exportindustrie im internationalen Wettbewerb*. Basle, Wepf, 1958.

Verein Deutsche Düngerfabrikanten. *Die Geschichte des Vereins in den letzten 25 Jahren: 1905–1930*. Hamburg, 1930.

Verein Deutscher Eisenhüttenleute. *100 Jahre VDE, 1860–1960*. Düsseldorf, Stahleisen, 1960.

Veyret-Verner, G. *L'industrie des Alpes françaises*. Paris, Arthaud, 1948.

Vigon, R. *Les industries chimiques de la banlieue nord de Paris*, (thesis, Faculté des Lettres). Paris, (typescript).

Vincent, L. and R. Froment. *Le progrès technique en France depuis cent ans*. (No. 3, Etudes spéciales de l'Institut de Conjoncture). Paris, Imprimerie Nationale, 1944.

Waller, P. *Probleme der deutschen chemischen Industrie*. Halberstadt, Mayer, 1928.

Weltausstellung in Chicago 1893. Amtlicher Bericht. Berlin, 1894.

Wichelhaus, H. *Wirtschaftliche Bedeutung chemischer Arbeit*. Braunschweig, Vieweg, 1893.

Wickel, H. *I. G. Deutschland: Ein Staat im Staate*. Berlin, Bücherkreis, 1932.

Williams, T. I. *The Chemical Industry*. London, Penguin Books, 1953.

Witt, O. Die Entwicklung der deutschen chemischen Industrie im 19. Jahrhundert. *Die Chemische Industrie*, no. 7, 1903.

Zart, A. *Die Entwicklung der chemischen Grossindustrie*. München–Berlin, K. Oldenbourg Verlag, 1922.

Index

24, 28ff., 31
role of market factors in, 42–52
and technical effort, 67–84
types of firms, 89–90, 92–94
role of, 103–106, 109, 112
and transmitted technical progress, 119, 128, 140, 132, 135
Frémy, of France, 68
Fuchsine, 36, 48–50, 76
affaire La Fuchsine, 35–36, 40, 46, 71ff. 81–82

Gas industry, 16ff., 74, 119, 143
Gay-Lussac, of France, 68
Geneva, 52
Germany, chemical industry in, 36–42, 53, 139–141
technical developments to 1914, 21ff., 27–30
role of market factors in, 44–52
and technical effort, 67–82
types of firms, 91, 93–97
role of, 103ff., 106, 108ff., 112
and transmitted technical progress, 120, 131, 135
Glass industry, 43, 93
Gold recovery, 30, 33, 108
Government, and technical effort, 71–75, 83, 139, 142, 146
Graebe–Lieberman synthesis, 71–72
Grandes Ecoles, 68ff.
Graphite electrodes, 31
Great Britain, chemical industry in, 35, 39, 140–141
technical developments to 1914, 21, 23ff., 26–30
role of market factors in, 47, 50, 52–53
and technical effort, 68–70, 74, 77
types of firms, 89
role of, 104ff., 112
and transmitted technical progress, 125ff.
Griesheim Elektron, 30, 94–95, 119
Guano, 29

Gustav Siegle, of Stuttgart, 129
Gypsum, 44, 108

Habakkuk, H. J., 140–141
Haber, L. F., 30, 55
Hall, of U.S., 31
Hamburg, 51
Heavy chemicals industry, 38, 43, 49, 51, 89–90, 92
of 1914, 24–25
Héroult, of France, 31
Heumann, 70
Höchst Company, 38, 40, 45–46, 122, 125
Hoffmann, W. G., 39, 70
Hydroelectricity, 30, 44, 108
Hydrosulfite bleaches, 122

IG-Farben, AG, 38, 76
Import, 52, 104–105, 146, 148
Indigo, synthesis of, 28, 77, 122
Industrial Revolution, 106
Inorganic chemicals industry, 52, 94
Inputs, 59, 103, 108
Interessengemeinschaft (IG), 91, 96ff.
Investment, gross
rate of, 145
Iron, 108

Japan, 104

Kalisyndikat, 96
Kekule, of Germany, 28, 69ff.
Kelp, 43
Key sector, 103
Knowledge and knowledge-centered firms, 89–97, 113, 140ff., 143–148
and technical effort, 60–67, 72, 75, 79–81, 83
and transmitted technical progress, 117ff., 120–135
Keynesian (demand-oriented) view, 105, 107
Konzern, 94
Krupp works, 127